Just 5

125 recipes
with 5 ingredients

About ◐Weight Watchers

Weight Watchers International, Inc., is the world's leading provider of weight-management services, operating globally through a network of company-owned and franchise operations. Weight Watchers holds nearly 50,000 weekly meetings worldwide, at which members receive group support and education about healthful eating patterns, behavior modification, and physical activity. Weight-loss and weight-management results vary by individual. We recommend that you attend Weight Watchers meetings to benefit from the supportive environment you find there and follow the comprehensive Weight Watchers program, which includes a food plan, an activity plan, and a behavioral component. In addition, Weight Watchers offers a wide range of products, publications, and programs for people interested in weight loss and weight control. For the Weight Watchers meeting nearest you, call **1-800-651-6000.** For information about bringing Weight Watchers to your workplace, call **1-800-8AT-WORK.** Also visit us at our Web site, **WeightWatchers.com**, and look for *Weight Watchers Magazine* at your newsstand or in your meeting room.

**Filet Mignon with Garlic Cream Sauce, page 40,
and Roast Tomatoes with Thyme and Olive Oil, page 169**

Weight Watchers Publishing Group

EDITORIAL DIRECTOR Nancy Gagliardi

CREATIVE DIRECTOR Ed Melnitsky

PRODUCTION MANAGER Alan Biederman

PHOTO EDITOR Deborah Hardt

MANAGING EDITOR Sarah Wharton

EDITORIAL ASSISTANT Katerina Gkionis

FOOD EDITOR Eileen Runyan

EDITOR Alice Thompson

NUTRITION CONSULTANT Jacqueline Kroon MS, RD

PHOTOGRAPHER Philip Friedman

FOOD STYLIST Susan Ottaviano

PROP STYLIST Laurent Laborie

COVER DESIGNER LeAnna Weller Smith

ART DIRECTOR Pauline Neuwirth

About Our Recipes

While losing weight isn't only about what you eat, Weight Watchers realizes the critical role it plays in your success and overall good health. That's why our philosophy is to offer great-tasting, easy recipes that are nutritious as well as delicious. We make every attempt to use wholesome ingredients and to ensure that our recipes fall within the recommendations of the U.S. Dietary Guidelines for Americans for a diet that promotes health and reduces the risk for disease. If you have special dietary needs, consult with your health-care professional for advice on a diet that is best for you, then adapt these recipes to meet your specific nutritional needs.

To achieve these good-health goals and get the maximum satisfaction from the foods you eat, we suggest you keep the following information in mind while preparing our recipes:

The *PointsPlus*™ Program and Good Nutrition

► Recipes in this book have been developed for Weight Watchers members who are following the *PointsPlus* program. *PointsPlus* values are given for each recipe. They're assigned based on the amount of protein (grams), carbohydrates (grams), fat (grams), and fiber (grams) contained in a single serving of a recipe.

► Recipes include approximate nutritional information; they are analyzed for Calories (Cal), Total Fat, Saturated Fat (Sat Fat), Trans Fat, Cholesterol (Chol), Sodium (Sod), Total Carbohydrates (Total Carb), Total Sugar, Dietary Fiber (Fib), Protein (Prot), and Calcium (Calc). The nutritional values are calculated by registered dietitians, using nutrition analysis software.

► Substitutions made to the ingredients will alter the per-serving nutritional information and may affect the *PointsPlus* value.

► Our recipes meet Weight Watchers Good Health Guidelines for eating lean proteins and fiber-rich whole grains, and having at least five servings of vegetables and fruits and two servings of low-fat or fat-free dairy products a day, while limiting your intake of saturated fat, sugar, and sodium.

- Health agencies recommend limiting sodium intake. To stay in line with this recommendation we keep sodium levels in our recipes reasonably low; to boost flavor, we often include fresh herbs or a squeeze of citrus instead of salt. If you don't have to restrict your sodium, feel free to add a touch more salt as desired.
- In the recipes a green triangle (▲) indicates Power Foods.
- ▲ Healthy Extra suggestions have a *PointsPlus* value of **0** unless otherwise stated.
- Recipes that work with the Simply Filling technique are listed on page 15. Find more details about this technique at your meeting.
- For information about the science behind lasting weight loss and more, please visit **WeightWatchers.com/science.**

Read this First: Shopping for Ingredients

As you learn to eat healthier and add more Power Foods to your meals, remember these tips for choosing foods wisely:

- **Lean Meats and Poultry** Purchase lean meats and poultry, and trim them of all visible fat before cooking. When poultry is cooked with the skin on, we recommend removing the skin before eating. Nutritional information for recipes that include meat, poultry, and fish is based on cooked, skinless boneless portions (unless otherwise stated), with the fat trimmed.
- **Seafood** Whenever possible, our recipes call for seafood that is sustainable and deemed the most healthful for human consumption so that your choice of seafood is not only good for the oceans but also good for you. For more information about the best seafood choices and to download a pocket guide, go to **environmentaldefensefund.org** or **montereybayaquarium.org.** For information about mercury and seafood go to **weightwatchers.com.**
- **Produce** For best flavor, maximum nutrient content, and the lowest prices, buy fresh, local produce, such as vegetables, leafy greens, and fruits in season. Rinse them thoroughly before using and keep a supply of cut-up vegetables and fruits in your refrigerator for convenient, healthy snacks.
- **Whole Grains** Explore your market for whole-grain products such as whole wheat and whole-grain breads and pastas, brown rice, bulgur, barley, cornmeal, whole wheat couscous, oats, and quinoa to enjoy with your meals.

Preparation and Measuring

- **Read the Recipe** Take a couple of minutes to read through the ingredients and directions before you start to prepare a recipe. This will prevent you from discovering midway through that you don't have an important ingredient or that a recipe requires several hours of marinating. And it's also a good idea to assemble all ingredients and utensils within easy reach before you begin a recipe.

▶ **Weighing and Measuring** The success of any recipe depends on accurate weighing and measuring. The effectiveness of the Weight Watchers program and the accuracy of the nutritional analysis depend on correct measuring as well. Use the following techniques:

- Weigh food such as meat, poultry, and fish on a food scale.
- To measure liquids, use a standard glass or plastic measuring cup placed on a level surface. For amounts less than ¼ cup, use standard measuring spoons.
- To measure dry ingredients, use metal or plastic measuring cups that come in ¼-, ⅓-, ½-, and 1-cup sizes. Fill the appropriate cup and level it with the flat edge of a knife or spatula. For amounts less than ¼ cup, use standard measuring spoons.

Cherry Fool, page 177

Contents

Recipes by *PointsPlus* value 11

Recipes that work with the Simply Filling technique 15

1 LIGHT MEALS 16
Soups, Salads, Sandwiches, and More

2 MARVELOUS MEATS 38
Beef, Pork, and Lamb

3 PERFECT POULTRY 62
Chicken, Turkey, and Duck

4 FROM THE SEA 88
Fabulous Fish and Shellfish

5 MEATLESS MAINS 110
Great Vegetarian Entrées

6 READY IN 20 MINUTES OR LESS 130
Easy Weeknight Wonders

7 Bonus Chapter!
THREE-INGREDIENT SIDES 152

8 SHORT & SWEET 170
Simple, Scrumptious Desserts

Index 199

Spaghetti "Bolognese," page 112

Recipes by *PointsPlus* value

1 *PointsPlus* value

Oven-Roasted Kale 167

Roast Tomatoes with Thyme and Olive Oil 169

Sautéed Escarole with Sun-Dried Tomatoes 165

2 *PointsPlus* value

Baby Greens with Gorgonzola and Almonds 28

Beet Salad with Pecan-Cheese Wedges 127

Broccolini with Walnuts and Shallots 168

Cantaloupe-Lime Granita 195

Chocolate-Coconut Truffles 190

Creamy Borscht with Tarragon 20

Eggplant–Goat Cheese Rolls 125

Ginger Beets 161

Lemon-Scented Macaroons 196

Parsnip Soup with Smoked Paprika 23

Raspberry-Nectarine Terrine 172

3 *PointsPlus* value

Buttermilk-Scallion Mashed Potatoes 156

Cherry Fool 177

Chicken, Cheddar, and Apple Panini 33

Chinese Egg-Flower Soup 18

Chocolate-Ricotta Mousse 188

Couscous with Dried Fruit and Pine Nuts 160

Crêpes with Ham, Spinach, and Leek 56

Grilled Pork Tenderloin with Orange and Rosemary 50

Lime-and-Chili–Grilled Shrimp 148

Maple-Glazed Butternut Squash 164

Mussels in Spicy Garlic Broth 105

Napa-Beef Slaw with Ginger Dressing 26

Pea Soup with Smoked Salmon 21

Silky Almond Flans 189

Souvlaki-Style Fish Kebabs 143

Tex-Mex Salmon Salad 30

Vanilla Bean Panna Cotta 185

Vegetarian Avgolemono with Dill 119

4 *PointsPlus* value

Artichoke and Garlic Bruschetta 36

Baked Whole Sea Bass with Fennel 95

Beefy Chili Verde with Poblanos 45

Berries with White Chocolate–Caramel Sauce 191

Blueberry-Buttermilk Cobbler 183

Cardamom-Coconut Rice 157

Chicken Cutlets with Lemon-Caper Sauce 137

Chicken Kebabs with Lime and Pineapple 71

Cinnamon-Apple Phyllo Purses 181

Coriander-Mint Lamb Chops 57

Curried Chicken Salad 25

Ginger-Sesame Steak Kebabs 132

Grilled Pork and Veggie Skewers 135

Grilled Turkey with Plums and Greens 141

Hoisin-Marinated London Broil 42

Kielbasa with Cabbage and Caraway 86

Mahimahi with Coconut Curry Sauce 100

Mediterranean Lamb Chops 136

Pan-Fried Shrimp in Red Pepper Sauce 103

Pan-Glazed Turkey Tenderloin 84

Pan-Toasted Reubens 31

Roasted Sweet Potatoes, Parsnips, and Onion 154

Rosemary-Balsamic Pork Chops 133

Sautéed Sweet Plantains 162

Soba-Noodle Soup with Miso 22

Spiced Brandy Custards 184

Spicy Blue Cheese Turkey Burgers 85

Spinach and Sun-Dried Tomato Pizza 149

Striped Bass with Warm Sherry Vinaigrette 101

Stuffed Portobello Mushrooms 114

Sweet-and-Spicy Roast Chicken 64

Sweet Chipotle Drumsticks 77

Vegetable-Cheese Frittata 118

Wild Rice Pilaf with Raisins and Orange 159

5 *PointsPlus* value

Catfish Amandine 99

Chicken Breasts with Garlic and Orange 65

Chicken Roulades with Prosciutto and Sage 69

Chicken with Black Bean Sauce 72

Chilled Pear Soup with Almonds 175

Chocolate Mousse with Sliced Strawberries 186

Egg and Broccoli Strudel 117

Grilled Flank Steak with Sweet Onions 43

Ham Steaks with Apples and Cranberries 55

Hearty Chicken-Barley Stew 76

Lemon-Cumin Halibut Steaks 146

Lobster Ravioli with Plum Tomato Sauce 104

Loin of Pork Stuffed with Cherries 53

Oven-Fried Chicken with Buttermilk Brine 73

Poached Salmon with Wasabi Mayonnaise 91

Pork Medallions with Marsala and Mushrooms 54

Red Lentil–and–Black Bean Masala 122

Roasted Eggplant and Cauliflower Curry 123

Scallop-Broccoli Stir-Fry 106

Simmered Italian-Style Pork Chops 51

Spicy Teriyaki Skirt Steak 44

Stuffed Clams with Shallots and Lemon 37

Tofu and Shiitake Stir-Fry 115

Tuna Teriyaki Burgers 142

6 *PointsPlus* value

Apricot-Oatmeal Crisp 180

Braised Chicken Thighs with Tomatoes and Green Olives 74

Beer-Braised Mussels 147

Caribbean Shrimp Tacos 35

Cinnamon-Poached Pears 174

Chicken-Chili Cobbler with Polenta 80

Chocolate–Chocolate Chip Sorbet 194

Crispy Pecan-Crusted Chicken Breasts 68

Duck with Cherry-Tarragon Glaze 87

Filet Mignon with Garlic Cream Sauce 40

Honey-Glazed Arctic Char 93

Niçoise-Style Tuna and Rice Salad 27

Pan-Grilled Tuna and Lemons over Arugula 94

Pesto-and-Feta–Stuffed Chicken Breasts 66

Roast Salmon with Cilantro and Lime 92

Smoked-Chicken and Mango Wraps 34

Seafood Salad with Lemon and Orzo 109

Swordfish Steaks with Caramelized
     Onions 96

Two-Tomato French Bread Pizzas 128

7 *PointsPlus* value

Braised Beef Shanks with Wine and
     Shallots 47

Coconut Turkey Fingers with Peach Sauce 82

Crispy Cornmeal-Coated Flounder 98

Frozen Coffee-Hazelnut Tarts 193

Pineapple Upside-Down Shortcakes 178

Smoky Greens and Beans with Polenta 120

8 *PointsPlus* value

Fried Rice with Snow Peas 151

Quick Chicken and Black Bean Burritos 138

Rigatoni with Spicy Sausage and Beans 61

9 *PointsPlus* value

Butterflied Lamb with Couscous Salad 58

Catfish Po' Boys 144

Pasta with Chicken Sausage and
     Artichokes 81

Spaghetti "Bolognese" 112

Tortellini with Chicken and Watercress 79

10 *PointsPlus* value

Beef and Ricotta Lasagna 48

Penne with Blue Cheese and Squash 126

Chicken Kebabs with Lime and Pineapple, page 71, and Oven-Roasted Kale, page 167

Recipes that work with the Simply Filling technique

Beefy Chili Verde with Poblanos 45

Chicken Breasts with Garlic and Orange 65

Chicken, Cheddar, and Apple Panini 33

Chicken Kebabs with Lime and Pineapple 71

Coriander-Mint Lamb Chops 57

Creamy Borscht with Tarragon 20

Curried Chicken Salad 25

Fried Rice with Snow Peas 151

Ginger Beets 161

Grilled Pork and Veggie Skewers 135

Grilled Turkey with Plums and Greens 141

Lemon-Cumin Halibut Steaks 146

Lime-and-Chili–Grilled Shrimp 148

Mediterranean Lamb Chops 136

Mussels in Spicy Garlic Broth 105

Oven-Roasted Kale 167

Pan-Grilled Tuna and Lemons over Arugula 94

Parsnip Soup with Smoked Paprika 23

Red Lentil–and–Black Bean Masala 122

Roasted Sweet Potatoes, Parsnips, and Onion 154

Roast Tomatoes with Thyme and Olive Oil 169

Sautéed Escarole with Sun-Dried Tomatoes 165

Scallop-Broccoli Stir-Fry 106

Seafood Salad with Lemon and Orzo 109

Souvlaki-Style Fish Kebabs 143

Striped Bass with Warm Sherry Vinaigrette 101

Tex-Mex Salmon Salad 30

Tuna Teriyaki Burgers 142

Vegetable-Cheese Frittata 118

Vegetarian Avgolemono with Dill 119

LIGHT MEALS

Soups, Salads, Sandwiches, and More

Chinese Egg-Flower Soup   **18**

Creamy Borscht with Tarragon   **20**

Pea Soup with Smoked Salmon   **21**

Soba-Noodle Soup with Miso   **22**

Parsnip Soup with Smoked Paprika   **23**

Curried Chicken Salad   **25**

Napa-Beef Slaw with Ginger Dressing   **26**

Niçoise-Style Tuna and Rice Salad   **27**

Baby Greens with Gorgonzola and Almonds   **28**

Tex-Mex Salmon Salad   **30**

Pan-Toasted Reubens   **31**

Chicken, Cheddar, and Apple Panini   **33**

Smoked-Chicken and Mango Wraps   **34**

Caribbean Shrimp Tacos   **35**

Artichoke and Garlic Bruschetta   **36**

Stuffed Clams with Shallots and Lemon   **37**

Chinese Egg-Flower Soup

▲ **4 cups reduced-sodium chicken broth**

+

3 tablespoons cornstarch

+

▲ **2 large eggs, lightly beaten**

+

1 teaspoon rice wine vinegar

+

▲ **1⅓ cups thawed frozen peas**

1 Bring broth to boil in large saucepan over medium heat. Whisk cornstarch and ¼ cup cold water in small cup until smooth; whisk cornstarch mixture into broth. Simmer until soup thickens slightly, about 2 minutes. Reduce heat until broth barely simmers. Slowly drizzle eggs into soup while stirring quickly in circular motion; cook 1 minute and remove from heat. Stir in vinegar.

2 Meanwhile, heat peas according to package directions and divide evenly among 4 bowls. Ladle soup over peas.

PER SERVING (1 ¼ cups soup and ⅓ cup peas):
340 g, 116 Cal, 2 g Total Fat, 1 g Sat Fat, 0 g Trans Fat, 108 mg Chol, 626 mg Sod, 14 g Total Carb, 3 g Total Sugar, 3 g Fib, 9 g Prot, 43 mg Calc.

Simple Additions   **Garnish this soup with a little chopped fresh cilantro and a drizzle of reduced-sodium soy sauce if you like.**

Chinese Egg-Flower Soup

Creamy Borscht with Tarragon

PREP 10 min | **COOK** 15 min | **SERVES** 6 | **LEVEL** Basic

▲ **3 cups reduced-sodium vegetable broth**

+

▲ **1 onion, diced**

+

▲ **2 (14½-ounce) cans no-salt-added sliced beets, with liquid**

+

▲ **¼ cup fat-free sour cream**

+

1 tablespoon chopped fresh tarragon

1 Combine broth, onion, and ¼ teaspoon black pepper in large saucepan over high heat; bring to boil. Reduce heat and simmer, uncovered, until onion is very tender, about 10 minutes. Remove saucepan from heat and carefully stir in beets. Pour soup into blender in batches and puree.

2 Return soup to saucepan and bring to simmer. Whisk in sour cream, ladle soup into bowls, and sprinkle with tarragon.

PER SERVING (1¼ cups): 293 g, 64 Cal, 0 g Total Fat, 0 g Sat Fat, 0 g Trans Fat, 1 mg Chol, 115 mg Sod, 14 g Total Carb, 9 g Total Sugar, 2 g Fib, 2 g Prot, 50 mg Calc.

PointsPlus® value
Per Serving

▲ Healthy Extra **Make this soup heartier by stirring in 6 ounces (1½ cups) cooked diced chicken breast after blending (the per-serving *PointsPlus* value will increase by *1*).**

Pea Soup with Smoked Salmon

PREP 10 min | **COOK** 20 min | **SERVES** 6 | **LEVEL** Basic

▲ **2 (14½-ounce) cans reduced-sodium chicken broth**

+

▲ **1 large baking potato, peeled and cubed**

+

▲ **1 large onion, diced**

+

▲ **1 (16-ounce) bag frozen peas**

+

2 ounces smoked salmon, cut into strips

1 Combine broth, potato, and onion in large saucepan; bring to boil over high heat. Reduce heat and simmer, uncovered, until potato is fork-tender, 8–10 minutes. Stir in peas; simmer until peas are bright green, about 5 minutes.

2 Remove saucepan from heat and let soup cool 5 minutes. Pour soup into blender in batches and puree. Return soup to saucepan and cook over high heat, stirring occasionally, just until heated through, about 2 minutes. Ladle into bowls, top with salmon, and sprinkle with cracked black pepper.

PER SERVING (1 cup soup and 1½ tablespoons salmon): 297 g, 133 Cal, 1 g Total Fat, 0 g Sat Fat, 0 g Trans Fat, 2 mg Chol, 449 mg Sod, 24 g Total Carb, 5 g Total Sugar, 5 g Fib, 9 g Prot, 40 mg Calc.

3 PointsPlus® value Per Serving

FYI **Use caution when blending hot liquids; the heat can cause air in the blender to expand, sometimes enough to blow the lid off and send scalding liquid all over your kitchen. Play it safe: Let the mixture cool 5 minutes and never fill the container more than half full, place the lid on securely, gently hold it down with a folded kitchen towel, and start blending on low speed.**

Soba-Noodle Soup with Miso

PREP 5 min | **COOK** 20 min | **SERVES** 6 | **LEVEL** Basic

6 ounces soba noodles

+

▲ **4 cups reduced-sodium vegetable broth**

+

1 tablespoon light miso

+

▲ **¼ pound shiitake mushrooms, stems discarded and caps sliced**

+

▲ **3 cups baby spinach**

1 Cook noodles according to package directions, omitting salt. Drain noodles, cool under cold running water, and drain again.

2 Whisk together broth, miso, and 1 cup water in large saucepan. Add mushrooms and bring to boil. Reduce heat and simmer, uncovered, until mushrooms are tender, about 6 minutes. Stir in noodles and spinach; cook until noodles are heated through and spinach is wilted, about 3 minutes.

PER SERVING (1 cup): 224 g, 129 Cal, 1 g Total Fat, 0 g Sat Fat, 0 g Trans Fat, 0 mg Chol, 461 mg Sod, 28 g Total Carb, 2 g Total Sugar, 1 g Fib, 5 g Prot, 32 mg Calc.

▲ Healthy Extra   **Add 1⅓ cups canned crabmeat to the soup along with the spinach (the per-serving *PointsPlus* value will increase by *1*).**

Parsnip Soup with Smoked Paprika

PREP 10 min | **COOK** 35 min | **SERVES** 6 | **LEVEL** Basic

▲ **6 cups reduced-sodium chicken broth**

▲ **1 pound parsnips, peeled and thinly sliced**

▲ **½ onion, chopped**

2 garlic cloves, finely chopped

1 teaspoon smoked paprika

1 Combine broth, parsnips, onion, and garlic in large saucepan; bring to boil. Reduce heat and simmer, uncovered, until parsnips are very tender, about 25 minutes.

2 Remove saucepan from heat and let soup cool 5 minutes. Pour soup into blender in batches and puree. Return soup to saucepan and simmer until heated through. Ladle into bowls and sprinkle with paprika.

PER SERVING (1 cup): 333 g, 80 Cal, 0 g Total Fat, 0 g Sat Fat, 0 g Trans Fat, 0 mg Chol, 563 mg Sod, 16 g Total Carb, 5 g Total Sugar, 3 g Fib, 5 g Prot, 54 mg Calc.

2 PointsPlus® value™

Per Serving

Simple Additions   **Chopped chives are an excellent garnish for this flavorful soup.**

Curried Chicken Salad

Curried Chicken Salad

PREP 10 min | **COOK** 10 min | **SERVES** 4 | **LEVEL** Basic

 1 pound skinless, boneless chicken breast

+

 ¼ cup fat-free Italian dressing

+

 1½ teaspoons curry powder

+

 1 (6-ounce) bag baby lettuce

+

 1 cup red grapes, halved

1 Cut chicken into ¾-inch pieces. Spray medium nonstick skillet with nonstick spray and set over medium-high heat. Sprinkle chicken with ¼ teaspoon salt and ⅛ teaspoon pepper and cook, turning occasionally, until cooked through, about 8 minutes.

2 Meanwhile, combine dressing and curry powder in large bowl. Add lettuce, grapes, and cooked chicken; toss to coat.

PER SERVING (2¼ cups): 169 g, 165 Cal, 3 g Total Fat, 1 g Sat Fat, 0 g Trans Fat, 63 mg Chol, 374 mg Sod, 11 g Total Carb, 8 g Total Sugar, 2 g Fib, 24 g Prot, 23 mg Calc.

4 PointsPlus® value
Per Serving

FYI   Toasting the curry powder before adding it to the dressing will intensify its flavor. Heat a small dry pan over medium heat just until hot; add the curry powder and stir just until fragrant, about 20 seconds. Immediately transfer the curry to a plate to cool.

Napa-Beef Slaw with Ginger Dressing

PREP 10 min | **COOK** none | **SERVES** 4 | **LEVEL** Basic

6 tablespoons reduced-calorie sesame-ginger dressing

+

2 teaspoons grated peeled fresh ginger

+

▲ 6 cups thinly sliced Napa cabbage

+

▲ 2 carrots, grated

+

▲ 6 (1-ounce) slices lean sirloin roast beef, trimmed and cut into strips

Whisk together dressing and ginger in large bowl. Add cabbage and carrot; toss to coat. Divide among 4 plates and top each evenly with roast beef.

PER SERVING (1¾ cups slaw and 1½ slices roast beef): 209 g, 131 Cal, 4 g Total Fat, 1 g Sat Fat, 0 g Trans Fat, 32 mg Chol, 344 mg Sod, 10 g Total Carb, 6 g Total Sugar, 2 g Fib, 14 g Prot, 73 mg Calc.

3 PointsPlus® value

Per Serving

▲ Healthy Extra **The addition of a diced red bell pepper and a few sliced scallions will add fiber, color, and flavor to your slaw without increasing the per-serving *PointsPlus* value.**

Niçoise-Style Tuna and Rice Salad

PREP 10 min | **COOK** none | **SERVES** 4 | **LEVEL** Basic

Zest and juice of 1 lemon

+

▲ **2 cups cooled cooked brown rice**

+

▲ **1 tomato, diced**

+

10 pitted niçoise olives, sliced

+

1 (6-ounce) can chunk light tuna in oil, drained well

In large bowl, combine lemon zest and 3 tablespoons of juice (reserve remaining juice for another use). Add rice, tomato, olives, and ¼ teaspoon black pepper; toss well. Gently stir in tuna.

PER SERVING (1 cup): 195 g, 230 Cal, 7 g Total Fat, 1 g Sat Fat, 0 g Trans Fat, 8 mg Chol, 177 mg Sod, 27 g Total Carb, 1 g Total Sugar, 3 g Fib, 15 g Prot, 27 mg Calc.

6 PointsPlus® value

Per Serving

- -

Simple Additions   **Add chopped fresh basil and a few teaspoons of drained capers to this tasty salad.**

Baby Greens with Gorgonzola and Almonds

PREP 5 min | **COOK** none | **SERVES** 4 | **LEVEL** Basic

 5 tablespoons raspberry fat-free vinaigrette

+

 1 thinly sliced shallot

+

 ▲ **1 (7-ounce) bag mixed spring greens**

+

¼ cup crumbled Gorgonzola cheese (1 ounce)

+

2 tablespoons chopped smoked almonds

Combine vinaigrette and shallot in large bowl. Add greens and toss to coat. Add Gorgonzola and toss again. Divide salad among 4 bowls or plates and sprinkle evenly with almonds.

PER SERVING (1½ cups salad and ½ tablespoon almonds): 93 g, 89 Cal, 4 g Total Fat, 2 g Sat Fat, 0 g Trans Fat, 10 mg Chol, 174 mg Sod, 10 g Total Carb, 5 g Total Sugar, 2 g Fib, 4 g Prot, 60 mg Calc.

2 PointsPlus® value

Per Serving

▲ Healthy Extra   **Add 1 cup of your favorite berries (raspberries, blackberries, or blueberries) and 1 cup thinly sliced fennel bulb along with the lettuce.**

Baby Greens with Gorgonzola and Almonds

Tex-Mex Salmon Salad

| PREP 5 min | COOK none | SERVES 2 | LEVEL Basic |

▲ **1 (5-ounce) can skinless, boneless pink salmon, drained**

▲ **2 scallions, thinly sliced**

▲ **¼ cup fat-free tomato salsa**

+

2 tablespoons chopped fresh cilantro

+

2 tablespoons fat-free mayonnaise

Put salmon in medium bowl and break into chunks with fork. Add remaining ingredients and gently toss until mixed.

PER SERVING (½ cup): 132 g, 117 Cal, 3 g Total Fat, 0 g Sat Fat, 0 g Trans Fat, 52 mg Chol, 521 mg Sod, 6 g Total Carb, 3 g Total Sugar, 1 g Fib, 18 g Prot, 12 mg Calc.

PointsPlus® value
Per Serving

▲ Healthy Extra **Serve this salad over a bed of your favorite lettuce for no change in the *PointsPlus* value, or try it between 2 slices of reduced-calorie whole wheat bread for an additional *3 PointsPlus* value per serving.**

Pan-Toasted Reubens

PREP 5 min | **COOK** 5 min | **SERVES** 4 | **LEVEL** Basic

▲ ⅓ cup
sauerkraut,
drained

+

4 slices
seedless rye
bread

+

2 tablespoons
reduced-fat
Thousand
Island dressing

+

4 (¾-ounce)
slices turkey
pastrami

+

▲ 2 (¾-ounce)
slices fat-free
Swiss cheese

1 Put sauerkraut in small strainer and rinse well, tossing, under running water. Squeeze dry.

2 Spray large nonstick skillet or griddle with nonstick spray and set over medium-low heat. Spread bread with dressing and layer 2 slices evenly with pastrami, sauerkraut, and cheese. Cover with remaining 2 slices and place Reubens on skillet. Cook until bread is toasted and cheese is melted, 2–3 minutes per side. Cut each Reuben in half and serve at once.

PER SERVING (½ sandwich): **92 g, 142 Cal, 3 g Total Fat, 1 g Sat Fat, 0 g Trans Fat, 18 mg Chol, 678 mg Sod, 19 g Total Carb, 3 g Total Sugar, 2 g Fib, 10 g Prot, 174 mg Calc.**

4
PointsPlus®
value™
Per Serving

FYI Tart, cured sauerkraut is classic in a Reuben, but in 10 minutes you can make a fresh, lower-salt substitution. Place 1½ cups very thinly sliced cabbage in a microwavable bowl and toss with 1 tablespoon water, ¼ teaspoon vinegar, and a pinch of salt. Microwave on High until tender, about 2 minutes, stopping once to stir. Cover bowl and cool 7 minutes; squeeze dry. You'll have ⅓ cup tasty sauerkraut-style cabbage, no rinsing required.

Chicken, Cheddar, and Apple Panini

Chicken, Cheddar, and Apple Panini

PREP 10 min | **COOK** 5 min | **SERVES** 4 | **LEVEL** Basic

▲ **4 slices reduced-calorie whole-grain bread**

+

1 tablespoon whole-grain mustard

+

▲ **¼ pound sliced cooked skinless chicken breast**

+

▲ **2 (¾-ounce) slices fat-free Cheddar cheese**

+

▲ **1 small Granny Smith apple, peeled, cored, and cut into thin slices**

1 Spray ridged grill pan with nonstick spray and set over medium-high heat or heat panini maker according to manufacturer's instructions.

2 Spread bread with mustard and layer 2 slices evenly with chicken, cheese, and apple. Cover with remaining 2 slices and place sandwiches on grill pan or panini maker. If using grill pan, weight sandwiches with heavy pan or skillet. Cook until bread is toasted and cheese is melted, about 3 minutes per side on grill pan, about 4 minutes total in panini maker. Cut each panini in half and serve at once.

PER SERVING (½ panini): 103 g, 122 Cal, 1 g Total Fat, 0 g Sat Fat, 0 g Trans Fat, 25 mg Chol, 273 mg Sod, 16 g Total Carb, 6 g Total Sugar, 4 g Fib, 14 g Prot, 176 mg Calc.

3 PointsPlus® value
Per Serving

▲ Healthy Extra **Serve each half panini with a few handfuls of baby arugula tossed with balsamic vinegar.**

Smoked-Chicken and Mango Wraps

▲ **1 ripe mango**

+

2 (8-inch) fat-free whole wheat tortillas

+

1 tablespoon fat-free mayonnaise

+

2 (1-ounce) slices smoked chicken breast

+

▲ **2 large green leaf lettuce leaves**

1 Slice flesh from pit of mango. Remove skin with paring knife; discard skin and cut flesh into thin slices.

2 Place tortillas on work surface; spread with mayonnaise and layer evenly with chicken, lettuce, and mango. Sprinkle with ⅛ teaspoon black pepper and roll up to enclose filling. Place each wrap on plate and cut in half on slight diagonal.

PER SERVING (1 wrap): 213 g, 209 Cal, 2 g Total Fat, 1 g Sat Fat, 0 g Trans Fat, 16 mg Chol, 316 mg Sod, 43 g Total Carb, 17 g Total Sugar, 6 g Fib, 10 g Prot, 20 mg Calc.

6 PointsPlus value
Per Serving

Simple Additions   **Sprinkle a few tablespoons of chopped fresh cilantro and a drop or two of your favorite hot sauce over each wrap before rolling it up.**

Caribbean Shrimp Tacos

PREP 15 min | **BAKE/COOK** 10 min | **SERVES** 4 | **LEVEL** Basic

8 (1½-ounce) taco shells

+

▲ **¾ pound medium shrimp, peeled and deveined**

+

▲ **1 small ripe papaya, halved, peeled, seeded, and diced**

+

½ small avocado, halved, peeled, pitted, and diced

+

2 teaspoons mango hot sauce

1 Preheat oven to 400°F. Place taco shells on baking sheet and bake until warm, about 8 minutes.

2 Meanwhile, spray large nonstick skillet with nonstick spray and set over medium-high heat. Add half of shrimp and cook, turning occasionally, just until opaque in center, 2–3 minutes. Transfer to bowl and repeat with remaining shrimp.

3 Spoon shrimp evenly into tacos. Top evenly with papaya, avocado, and hot sauce.

PER SERVING (2 tacos): 148 g, 227 Cal, 9 g Total Fat, 2 g Sat Fat, 1 g Trans Fat, 126 mg Chol, 308 mg Sod, 21 g Total Carb, 3 g Total Sugar, 3 g Fib, 16 g Prot, 62 mg Calc.

6 PointsPlus value
Per Serving

FYI   **Mango hot sauce is available in most supermarkets, but you can substitute plain hot sauce if you prefer.**

Artichoke and Garlic Bruschetta

PREP 10 min | **COOK/BROIL** 10 min | **SERVES** 6 | **LEVEL** Basic

2 teaspoons olive oil

+

▲ **2 (14-ounce) cans water-packed artichoke hearts, drained**

+

3 garlic cloves, thinly sliced

+

⅛ teaspoon red pepper flakes

+

1 small whole wheat baguette (8 ounces)

1 Heat oil in large nonstick skillet over medium-high heat. Rinse artichoke hearts; pat dry with paper towels, cut each into quarters, and add to skillet. Cook, stirring occasionally, just until artichokes begin to brown, about 4 minutes. Stir in garlic, red pepper flakes, and ⅛ teaspoon salt; cook, stirring occasionally, until garlic is golden, 2–3 minutes.

2 Meanwhile, preheat broiler. Cut off ends of baguette; discard or save for another use. Slice baguette on diagonal into 12 slices; broil just until golden, about 30 seconds per side. Top each slice with 2 tablespoons artichoke mixture.

PER SERVING (2 bruschetta): 173 g, 165 Cal, 3 g Total Fat, 0 g Sat Fat, 0 g Trans Fat, 0 mg Chol, 484 mg Sod, 28 g Total Carb, 1 g Total Sugar, 2 g Fib, 7 g Prot, 3 mg Calc.

▲ Healthy Extra   **Make this dish special by stirring in 1 (6-ounce) can crabmeat, drained, along with the garlic. Place 1 cup watercress sprigs on each plate and top with the bruschetta. (The per-serving *PointsPlus* value will increase by *1*.)**

Stuffed Clams with Shallots and Lemon

PREP 20 min | **COOK/BROIL** 10 min | **SERVES** 2 | **LEVEL** Advanced

2 slices firm whole wheat bread

+

1 teaspoon olive oil

+

2 shallots, minced

+

1 lemon

+

▲ 1 dozen littleneck clams, scrubbed and shucked, 12 half shells reserved

1 Put bread in food processor and pulse until medium crumbs form, about 30 seconds.

2 Heat oil in medium nonstick skillet over medium heat. Add shallots and cook, stirring constantly, until they begin to soften, about 2 minutes. Stir in bread crumbs and cook, stirring, 1 minute longer. Remove skillet from heat. Grate zest of half of lemon over bread crumb mixture and toss to combine.

3 Line broiler pan with aluminum foil and preheat broiler.

4 Place 12 reserved half shells on broiler pan and place meat of 1 clam in each. Top evenly with bread crumb mixture, lightly pressing down as needed. Lightly spray with nonstick spray. Broil 5 inches from heat until tops are golden and clams are cooked through, 6–7 minutes. Divide clams between 2 plates; slice lemon into wedges and serve with clams.

PER SERVING (6 clams): 148 g, 205 Cal, 5 g Total Fat, 1 g Sat Fat, 0 g Trans Fat, 38 mg Chol, 200 mg Sod, 23 g Total Carb, 3 g Total Sugar, 3 g Fib, 19 g Prot, 105 mg Calc.

5 PointsPlus® value
Per Serving

FYI **Bread that's slightly dry or a couple of days past fresh is ideal for making crumbs. If you think your bread is too moist and fresh, toast it briefly in your toaster on the lightest setting.**

MARVELOUS MEATS

Beef, Pork, and Lamb

Filet Mignon with Garlic Cream Sauce   **40**

Hoisin-Marinated London Broil   **42**

Grilled Flank Steak with Sweet Onions   **43**

Spicy Teriyaki Skirt Steak   **44**

Beefy Chili Verde with Poblanos   **45**

Braised Beef Shanks with Wine and Shallots   **47**

Beef and Ricotta Lasagna   **48**

Grilled Pork Tenderloin with Orange and Rosemary   **50**

Simmered Italian-Style Pork Chops   **51**

Loin of Pork Stuffed with Cherries   **53**

Pork Medallions with Marsala and Mushrooms   **54**

Ham Steaks with Apples and Cranberries   **55**

Crêpes with Ham, Spinach, and Leek   **56**

Coriander-Mint Lamb Chops   **57**

Butterflied Lamb with Couscous Salad   **58**

Rigatoni with Spicy Sausage and Beans   **61**

Filet Mignon with Garlic Cream Sauce

| PREP 5 min | COOK 10 min | SERVES 4 | LEVEL Basic |

▲ **4 (¼-pound) filets mignons, trimmed**

+

2 teaspoons olive oil

+

3 garlic cloves, minced

+

½ cup dry white wine or reduced-sodium chicken broth

+

2 tablespoons reduced-fat garlic-and-herb spreadable cheese

1 Sprinkle steaks evenly with ⅛ teaspoon salt and ¼ teaspoon cracked pepper. Heat large skillet over medium-high heat and add oil. Place steaks in skillet and cook until instant-read thermometer inserted into sides of steaks registers 145°F for medium rare, 3–4 minutes per side. Transfer to cutting board; loosely cover with foil and keep warm.

2 Return skillet to medium-high heat. Add garlic and cook, stirring, until softened, about 1 minute. Stir in wine and cook, scraping up browned bits from bottom of skillet, until mixture is reduced to about ¼ cup, 3–4 minutes. Remove skillet from heat; add cheese and stir until melted. Spoon sauce over steaks.

PER SERVING (1 steak and 1½ tablespoons sauce): 126 g, 227 Cal, 10 g Total Fat, 4 g Sat Fat, 0 g Trans Fat, 72 mg Chol, 163 mg Sod, 2 g Total Carb, 1 g Total Sugar, 0 g Fib, 25 g Prot, 45 mg Calc.

6 PointsPlus® value
Per Serving

▲ Healthy Extra   **Craving surf and turf? Add ½ cup steamed shrimp (2 ounces, or about 4 large shrimp) to each serving (and increase the *PointsPlus* value by 2).**

**Filet Mignon with Garlic Cream Sauce
and Roast Tomatoes with Thyme and Olive Oil, page 169**

Hoisin-Marinated London Broil

3 tablespoons hoisin sauce

2 garlic cloves, minced

2 teaspoons grated peeled fresh ginger

2 teaspoons unseasoned rice vinegar

▲ 1 pound boneless sirloin steak, trimmed

1 Combine hoisin sauce, garlic, ginger, and vinegar in zip-close plastic bag; add steak. Squeeze out air and seal bag; turn to coat steak. Refrigerate, turning bag occasionally, at least 2 hours or up to 2 days.

2 Spray broiler rack with nonstick spray and preheat broiler.

3 Remove steak from marinade; discard marinade. Pat steak dry with paper towels and place on broiler rack. Broil steak 5 inches from heat until instant-read thermometer inserted into side of steak registers 145°F for medium rare, 5–6 minutes per side. Transfer to cutting board and let stand 10 minutes. Cut steak across grain into 12 slices.

PER SERVING (3 slices London broil): 102 g, 186 Cal, 5 g Total Fat, 2 g Sat Fat, 0 g Trans Fat, 50 mg Chol, 249 mg Sod, 6 g Total Carb, 3 g Total Sugar, 0 g Fib, 26 g Prot, 24 mg Calc.

4 PointsPlus value
Per Serving

▲ Healthy Extra   **Serve this tangy steak with baked sweet potatoes drizzled with a few drops of reduced-sodium soy sauce for an East-West treat (1 medium [4½-ounce] sweet potato has a** *PointsPlus* **value of 3).**

Grilled Flank Steak with Sweet Onions

PREP 10 min | **GRILL** 10 min | **SERVES** 4 | **LEVEL** Basic

▲ **1 (1-pound) flank steak, trimmed**

+

3 teaspoons Cajun seasoning

+

▲ **2 large sweet onions, thickly sliced**

+

¼ cup chopped fresh cilantro

1 Spray grill rack with nonstick spray; preheat grill to medium or prepare medium fire.

2 Sprinkle steak with 2 teaspoons Cajun seasoning. Sprinkle onion slices with remaining 1 teaspoon seasoning. Lightly spray onions with nonstick spray. Place steak and onion slices on grill rack and grill until onions are browned and instant-read thermometer inserted into side of steak registers 145°F for medium rare, about 5 minutes per side.

3 Transfer steak to cutting board and let stand 10 minutes. Cut across grain into 16 slices. Sprinkle with cilantro and serve with onions.

PER SERVING (4 slices flank steak and 2 slices onion):
162 g, 189 Cal, 7 g Total Fat, 3 g Sat Fat, 0 g Trans Fat, 42 mg Chol, 457 mg Sod, 7 g Total Carb, 3 g Total Sugar, 1 g Fib, 25 g Prot, 33 mg Calc.

5 PointsPlus® value
Per Serving

▲ **Healthy Extra** Serve this steak with a quick, colorful corn salsa by combining 1 cup cooked corn kernels, 1 diced tomato, ¼ cup diced red onion, and ½ teaspoon red wine vinegar (one fourth of the salsa will have a *PointsPlus* value of *1*).

Spicy Teriyaki Skirt Steak

PREP 10 min | **BROIL** 10 min | **SERVES** 4 | **LEVEL** Basic

¼ **cup teriyaki sauce**

+

4 **garlic cloves, minced**

+

▲ 1 **Thai red chile pepper or other chile, seeded and minced**

+

1 **orange**

+

1 (1-pound) **skirt steak, trimmed**

1 Combine teriyaki sauce, garlic, and chile in zip-close plastic bag. Remove zest from orange with a zester and set aside. Measure out 2 tablespoons orange juice and add to bag (reserve remaining orange for another use). Add steak to bag. Squeeze out air and seal bag; turn to coat steak. Refrigerate, turning bag occasionally, at least 2 hours or overnight.

2 Spray broiler rack with nonstick spray and preheat broiler.

3 Remove steak from marinade; discard marinade. Place steak on broiler rack and broil 5 inches from heat until instant-read thermometer inserted into side of steak registers 145°F for medium rare, about 4 minutes per side.

4 Transfer steak to cutting board and let stand 10 minutes. Cut across grain into 16 slices. Sprinkle with reserved orange zest.

PER SERVING (4 slices steak): 128 g, 207 Cal, 9 g Total Fat, 3 g Sat Fat, 0 g Trans Fat, 50 mg Chol, 756 mg Sod, 6 g Total Carb, 3 g Total Sugar, 1 g Fib, 24 g Prot, 26 mg Calc.

5 PointsPlus® value
Per Serving

FYI **This is also an excellent recipe to try with flank steak.**

Beefy Chili Verde with Poblanos

PREP 5 min | **COOK** 20 min | **SERVES** 4 | **LEVEL** Basic

▲ ¾ **pound ground extra-lean beef (5% fat or less)**

+

▲ 2 **poblano peppers, seeded and coarsely chopped**

+

3 **garlic cloves, finely chopped**

+

1 **tablespoon chili powder**

+

▲ 1 **(16-ounce) jar fat-free salsa verde**

1 Spray large nonstick skillet with nonstick spray and set over medium-high heat. Add beef and cook, breaking it apart with wooden spoon, until browned, about 6 minutes.

2 Stir in poblanos and garlic; cook, stirring frequently, until peppers are tender, about 4 minutes. Stir in chili powder, salsa, and ½ cup water; bring to boil. Reduce heat and simmer until flavors are blended, about 10 minutes.

PER SERVING (1 cup): 184 g, 184 Cal, 6 g Total Fat, 2 g Sat Fat, 0 g Trans Fat, 51 mg Chol, 508 mg Sod, 14 g Total Carb, 4 g Total Sugar, 3 g Fib, 18 g Prot, 20 mg Calc.

4 PointsPlus® value™
Per Serving

FYI   **The oils from spicy chile peppers like poblanos can burn your flesh, so be sure to avoid touching the peppers themselves. It's safest to wear disposable plastic gloves when seeding and chopping chile peppers.**

Braised Beef Shanks with Wine and Shallots

Braised Beef Shanks
with Wine and Shallots

PREP 5 min | **COOK/BAKE** 2 hr | **SERVES** 4 | **LEVEL** Intermediate

4 (5-ounce) beef shanks, trimmed

+

3 shallots, chopped

+

▲ **1 (14½-ounce) can no-salt-added diced tomatoes**

+

¾ cup dry red wine

+

▲ **¾ cup reduced-sodium beef broth**

1 Preheat oven to 300°F.

2 Spray Dutch oven with nonstick spray and set over medium-high heat. Sprinkle shanks with ¼ teaspoon salt and ⅛ teaspoon black pepper. Add to Dutch oven and cook until browned, about 3 minutes per side. Transfer to plate.

3 Add shallots to Dutch oven and cook, stirring, until soft, about 4 minutes. Stir in tomatoes, wine, and broth, scraping up browned bits from bottom of pan. Bring mixture to boil and cook 3 minutes. Add shanks, ¼ teaspoon salt, and ⅛ teaspoon pepper. Cover and transfer pot to oven. Cook until shanks are fork-tender, about 1 hour 45 minutes.

4 Remove shanks from pot with slotted spoon; skim off and discard any fat from surface of sauce. Serve sauce over shanks.

PER SERVING (1 beef shank and generous ½ cup sauce):
357 g, 267 Cal, 6 g Total Fat, 2 g Sat Fat, 0 g Trans Fat, 55 mg Chol, 264 mg Sod, 10 g Total Carb, 4 g Total Sugar, 1 g Fib, 33 g Prot, 58 mg Calc.

7 PointsPlus® value Per Serving

Simple Additions   **Garnish the shanks with lots of fragrant fresh thyme.**

Beef and Ricotta Lasagna

PREP 20 min | **COOK/BAKE** 55 min | **SERVES** 8 | **LEVEL** Intermediate

▲ **1½ pounds ground lean beef (7% fat or less)**

+

4 cups no-salt-added marinara sauce

+

1 (8-ounce) box no-boil lasagna noodles (12 noodles)

+

▲ **2½ cups fat-free ricotta cheese**

+

1¼ cups grated reduced-fat mozzarella cheese

1 Preheat oven to 375°F; spray 9 x 13-inch baking dish with nonstick spray.

2 Spray large nonstick skillet with nonstick spray and set over medium-high heat. Add beef, ¼ teaspoon salt, and ¼ teaspoon black pepper; cook, breaking up beef with wooden spoon, until beef is browned and all liquid is evaporated, about 10 minutes. Tilt skillet to drain off any fat that might be left in pan.

3 Spread 1 cup marinara sauce over bottom of baking dish. Cover with 4 lasagna noodles, overlapping them slightly as needed. Cover with half of beef, dot with 1¼ cups ricotta, and spread another 1 cup marinara sauce on top. Add another 4 noodles and cover with remaining beef, remaining 1¼ cups ricotta, another 1 cup marinara sauce, and remaining 4 noodles. Spread remaining 1 cup marinara sauce on top and sprinkle with mozzarella.

4 Spray sheet of foil with nonstick spray; cover dish with foil and bake lasagna 30 minutes. Remove foil and continue to bake until mozzarella browns slightly and noodles are very tender, about 15 minutes longer. Cool 15 minutes and cut into 8 squares.

PER SERVING (1 square): 336 g, 396 Cal, 10 g Total Fat, 4 g Sat Fat, 0 g Trans Fat, 78 mg Chol, 447 mg Sod, 33 g Total Carb, 9 g Total Sugar, 2 g Fib, 43 g Prot, 527 mg Calc.

10 PointsPlus® value — Per Serving

▲ Healthy Extra   **Remove the beef from the skillet after you've browned it and add 2 cups sliced mushrooms and ½ cup diced onion to the skillet. Cook the vegetables over medium heat, stirring frequently, until the mushrooms release their liquid and brown slightly. Mix these vegetables into the beef for more great flavor and nutrition.**

Beef and Ricotta Lasagna

Grilled Pork Tenderloin
with Orange and Rosemary

PREP 10 min | **GRILL** 25 min | **SERVES** 4 | **LEVEL** Basic

2 garlic cloves, minced

+

1 tablespoon chopped fresh rosemary

+

1 teaspoon olive oil

+

Zest and juice of 1 orange

+

▲ 1 (1-pound) pork tenderloin, trimmed

1 Combine garlic, rosemary, olive oil, orange zest, and juice from half orange in zip-close plastic bag (reserve remaining orange half for another use); add pork. Squeeze out air and seal bag; turn to coat pork. Refrigerate, turning bag occasionally, at least 1 hour or overnight.

2 Spray grill rack with nonstick spray; preheat grill to medium or prepare medium fire. Sprinkle pork with ½ teaspoon salt and ¼ teaspoon black pepper. Place on grill rack and grill, turning occasionally, until instant-read thermometer inserted into center of pork registers 160°F, about 25 minutes.

3 Transfer pork to cutting board and let stand 5 minutes. Cut into 12 slices.

PER SERVING (3 slices pork): 103 g, 144 Cal, 4 g Total Fat, 1 g Sat Fat, 0 g Trans Fat, 62 mg Chol, 340 mg Sod, 3 g Total Carb, 1 g Total Sugar, 0 g Fib, 23 g Prot, 16 mg Calc.

3 PointsPlus® value ™ / Per Serving

Simple Additions **Garnish each serving with an orange wedge and a sprig of fresh rosemary.**

Simmered Italian-Style Pork Chops

PREP 10 min | **COOK** 15 min | **SERVES** 4 | **LEVEL** Basic

▲ **4 (¼-pound) boneless center-cut pork loin chops, trimmed**

+

2 garlic cloves, sliced

+

▲ **1 onion, chopped**

+

▲ **1 green bell pepper, chopped**

+

1 cup spicy marinara sauce

1 Spray large nonstick skillet with nonstick spray and set over medium-high heat. Sprinkle pork with ¼ teaspoon salt and ¼ teaspoon black pepper. Add to skillet and cook until browned, 2–3 minutes per side. Transfer to plate.

2 Add garlic, onion, and bell pepper to skillet; cook until vegetables begin to soften, about 3 minutes. Add marinara sauce and pork chops; turn pork to coat with sauce. Reduce heat and simmer until instant-read thermometer inserted into side of each chop registers 160°F, about 5 minutes.

PER SERVING (1 pork chop with ⅔ cup sauce): 211 g, 203 Cal, 8 g Total Fat, 2 g Sat Fat, 0 g Trans Fat, 66 mg Chol, 582 mg Sod, 10 g Total Carb, 6 g Total Sugar, 2 g Fib, 23 g Prot, 55 mg Calc.

5 PointsPlus© value
Per Serving

Simple Additions **Add 1 tablespoon drained capers to the sauce and garnish each serving with chopped fresh basil.**

Loin of Pork Stuffed with Cherries

Loin of Pork Stuffed with Cherries

PREP 30 min | **COOK/ROAST** 1 hr 10 min | **SERVES** 6 | **LEVEL** Advanced

⅓ **cup dried cherries, chopped**

3 tablespoons dried whole wheat bread crumbs

4 teaspoons chopped fresh thyme

½ **cup no-sugar-added cherry preserves**

▲ 1 (1½-pound) **boneless center-cut pork loin, trimmed**

1 Preheat oven to 400°F. Place rack in roasting pan and spray rack and pan with nonstick spray.

2 To make stuffing, place cherries in small bowl. Add boiling water to cover and soak cherries 10 minutes; drain. Return cherries to bowl and stir in bread crumbs, thyme, and ¼ cup preserves.

3 Cut pork in half lengthwise, leaving ½-inch hinge (do not cut all the way through). Open up pork like a book. Place, cut side down, between 2 sheets wax paper; gently pound with wooden mallet or rolling pin until meat is ½ inch thick. Remove top sheet of wax paper; sprinkle pork with ¾ teaspoon salt and ¼ teaspoon black pepper. Turn pork cut side up. Spoon stuffing in a line down center. Fold pork over filling and roll up to enclose; tie securely in 3 or 4 places with kitchen string.

4 Place pork on rack and roast 45 minutes. Brush with 1 tablespoon preserves and roast 5 minutes. Repeat brushing and roasting 3 more times with remaining 3 tablespoons preserves. Continue roasting until instant-read thermometer inserted into center of pork registers 160°F, about 5 minutes longer. Transfer pork to cutting board and let stand 10 minutes. Remove string; cut into 12 slices.

PER SERVING (2 slices pork): 115 g, 214 Cal, 6 g Total Fat, 2 g Sat Fat, 0 g Trans Fat, 66 mg Chol, 365 mg Sod, 15 g Total Carb, 11 g Total Sugar, 1 g Fib, 22 g Prot, 32 mg Calc.

▲ Healthy Extra **Serve this excellent pork with a side of steamed green beans sprinkled with lemon juice.**

Pork Medallions with Marsala and Mushrooms

PREP 20 min | **COOK** 20 min | **SERVES** 4 | **LEVEL** Intermediate

▲ **1 (1-pound) pork tenderloin, trimmed**

+

▲ **½ pound mixed wild mushrooms, sliced**

+

2 shallots, sliced

+

⅓ cup Marsala wine or apple juice

+

▲ **½ cup reduced-sodium chicken broth**

1 Cut pork into 8 equal pieces. Place 1 piece between 2 sheets wax paper; gently pound with wooden mallet or rolling pin until ½ inch thick. Repeat with remaining pork pieces.

2 Spray large nonstick skillet with nonstick spray and set over medium-high heat. Sprinkle pork with ¼ teaspoon salt and ¼ teaspoon black pepper; add to skillet and cook until browned and cooked through, about 3 minutes per side. Transfer to platter and keep warm.

3 Add mushrooms, shallots, ¼ teaspoon salt, and ¼ teaspoon black pepper to skillet. Cook, stirring frequently, until mushrooms are browned, about 5 minutes. Add wine, scraping up browned bits from bottom of skillet. Cook until liquid is almost completely evaporated, about 4 minutes longer. Add broth and boil 3 minutes. Spoon mixture over pork.

PER SERVING (2 pieces pork and ⅓ cup mushrooms and sauce): 208 g, 186 Cal, 3 g Total Fat, 1 g Sat Fat, 0 g Trans Fat, 62 mg Chol, 355 mg Sod, 8 g Total Carb, 3 g Total Sugar, 0 g Fib, 25 g Prot, 3 g Alcohol, 25 mg Calc.

5 PointsPlus® value Per Serving

▲ Healthy Extra **Serve this tasty pork dish with a side of whole wheat orzo (½ cup cooked whole wheat orzo per serving will increase the *PointsPlus* value by 2).**

Ham Steaks with Apples and Cranberries

PREP 10 min | **COOK** 15 min | **SERVES** 4 | **LEVEL** Basic

▲ **1 (10-ounce) low-sodium lean ham steak, trimmed**

+

▲ **2 large apples, peeled, cored, and diced**

+

▲ **1 onion, chopped**

+

▲ **1 cup low-sodium chicken broth**

+

¼ cup dried cranberries

1 Spray large skillet with nonstick spray and set over medium-high heat. Cut ham into 4 equal pieces and add to skillet. Cook until browned and heated through, about 2 minutes per side. Transfer to platter and keep warm.

2 Add apples, onion, and ¼ teaspoon black pepper to skillet; cook, covered, stirring occasionally, until soft, about 5 minutes. Add broth and cranberries; bring to boil. Reduce heat and simmer, uncovered, until most of broth has evaporated, about 5 minutes. Spoon mixture over ham.

PER SERVING (1 piece ham and ½ cup apple mixture): 284 g, 200 Cal, 5 g Total Fat, 1 g Sat Fat, 0 g Trans Fat, 38 mg Chol, 706 mg Sod, 25 g Total Carb, 18 g Total Sugar, 3 g Fib, 17 g Prot, 24 mg Calc.

5 PointsPlus® value

Per Serving

▲ Healthy Extra **A side of pureed butternut squash is a colorful, healthful accompaniment to this pork dish.**

Crêpes with Ham, Spinach, and Leek

PREP 10 min | **COOK** 20 min | **SERVES** 4 | **LEVEL** Intermediate

▲ **1 (5-ounce) bag baby spinach leaves**

+

▲ **1 large leek, white part only**

+

▲ **1 cup diced low-sodium lean ham (¼ pound)**

+

¼ pound fat-free cream cheese

+

4 (7-inch) crêpes

1 Combine spinach, ⅛ teaspoon salt, ⅛ teaspoon pepper, and ¼ cup water in large nonstick skillet over medium heat. Cook, covered, stirring frequently, until spinach is wilted and very soft, about 7 minutes. Drain in sieve, pressing with back of spoon to remove excess liquid.

2 Halve leek lengthwise and rinse well under cold running water, spreading layers to remove any sand or dirt. Pat dry and cut into thin slices.

3 Wipe out skillet, spray with nonstick spray, and set over medium-high heat. Add leek and cook, covered, stirring frequently, until tender, about 8 minutes. Add ham and spinach; cook, uncovered, stirring occasionally, until heated through, 2–3 minutes. Add cream cheese; cook, stirring frequently, until melted, 1–2 minutes longer.

4 Heat crêpes according to package directions. Spoon one fourth of filling onto each crêpe and roll up to enclose filling. Serve at once.

PER SERVING (1 crêpe): 142 g, 130 Cal, 3 g Total Fat, 1 g Sat Fat, 0 g Trans Fat, 23 mg Chol, 658 mg Sod, 15 g Total Carb, 4 g Total Sugar, 2 g Fib, 13 g Prot, 141 mg Calc.

3 PointsPlus® value

Per Serving

Simple Additions   **For flavor and color, cook a thinly sliced shallot along with the spinach and garnish the crêpes with a sprinkling of a chopped fresh leafy herb: Parsley, chervil, and dill are excellent choices.**

Coriander-Mint Lamb Chops

PREP 10 min | **BROIL** 5 min | **SERVES** 4 | **LEVEL** Basic

1¼ teaspoons
coriander seeds,
crushed

+

+

1 garlic clove,
minced

+

▲ 4 (¼-pound)
bone-in baby
lamb chops,
trimmed

+

2 tablespoons
chopped fresh
mint

1 Spray broiler rack with nonstick spray and preheat broiler.

2 Combine coriander, garlic, ½ teaspoon salt, and ¼ teaspoon black pepper in cup. Sprinkle mixture all over lamb, gently pressing to help it adhere. Place chops on boiler rack and broil 5 inches from heat until instant-read thermometer inserted into center of each chop registers 145°F for medium rare, about 3 minutes per side. Sprinkle with mint.

PER SERVING (1 lamb chop): 88 g, 173 Cal, 9 g Total Fat, 4 g Sat Fat, 0 g Trans Fat, 80 mg Chol, 332 mg Sod, 1 g Total Carb, 0 g Total Sugar, 0 g Fib, 21 g Prot, 21 mg Calc.

4 PointsPlus® value™ Per Serving

FYI   **Small seeds like coriander, fennel, and cumin can be crushed using a spice grinder or mortar and pestle. Or you can place them in a zip-close plastic bag, seal the bag, and very gently pound with the bottom of a small heavy pot or with a rolling pin.**

Butterflied Lamb with Couscous Salad

PREP 10 min | **COOK** 15 min | **SERVES** 4 | **LEVEL** Basic

▲ **1 cup whole wheat couscous**

+

1 teaspoon olive oil

+

▲ **1 tomato, halved, peeled, seeded, and diced**

+

¼ cup chopped fresh flat-leaf parsley

+

1 (1-pound) boneless leg of lamb, butterflied by butcher and trimmed

1 Cook couscous according to package directions, omitting salt. Allow to cool slightly. Drizzle with oil and gently stir to coat. Add tomato, parsley, and ¼ teaspoon salt; toss to coat.

2 Meanwhile, spray ridged grill pan with nonstick spray and set over medium-high heat. When pan is very hot, sprinkle lamb with ¼ teaspoon salt and ¼ teaspoon black pepper. Place on pan and cook until instant-read thermometer inserted into side of lamb registers 145°F for medium rare, about 7 minutes per side.

3 Transfer lamb to cutting board; let stand 10 minutes. Cut across grain into 12 slices and serve with couscous.

PER SERVING (3 slices lamb and ¾ cup salad):
179 g, 367 Cal, 14 g Total Fat, 5 g Sat Fat, 0 g Trans Fat, 119 mg Chol, 388 mg Sod, 24 g Total Carb, 1 g Total Sugar, 4 g Fib, 36 g Prot, 34 mg Calc.

9 PointsPlus® value
Per Serving

▲ Healthy Extra   **Stir 1 peeled diced cucumber, ¼ cup diced red onion, and 1 tablespoon lemon juice into the couscous along with the tomato.**

Butterflied Lamb with Couscous Salad

Rigatoni with Spicy Sausage and Beans

Rigatoni with Spicy Sausage and Beans

PREP 10 min | **COOK** 20 min | **SERVES** 6 | **LEVEL** Intermediate

▲ ½ **pound whole wheat rigatoni**

+

¾ **pound spicy Italian sausages (about 4), sliced**

+

▲ 1 (¾-**pound) bunch kale, stems removed and leaves thinly sliced**

+

▲ 1 (14½-**ounce) can low-sodium chicken broth**

+

▲ 1 (15½-**ounce) can no-salt-added red beans, rinsed and drained**

1 Cook pasta according to package directions, omitting salt.

2 Meanwhile, to make sauce, spray large nonstick saucepan with nonstick spray and set over medium-high heat. Add sausage and cook, stirring occasionally, until cooked through, about 5 minutes. Add kale and broth; bring to boil. Reduce heat and simmer until kale is tender, about 5 minutes. Add beans and simmer, uncovered, until liquid is reduced by half, about 5 minutes longer.

3 Add pasta to sauce. Cook, stirring occasionally, until well mixed, about 1 minute.

PER SERVING (1½ cups): 265 g, 332 Cal, 10 g Total Fat, 3 g Sat Fat, 0 g Trans Fat, 16 mg Chol, 415 mg Sod, 45 g Total Carb, 2 g Total Sugar, 7 g Fib, 17 g Prot, 116 mg Calc.

8 PointsPlus® value
Per Serving

Simple Additions   **Garlic lovers may wish to add a few cloves of sliced garlic to the pan just before adding the kale. And those who really love heat can sprinkle a pinch or two of red pepper flakes over the finished dish.**

PERFECT POULTRY

Chicken, Turkey, and Duck

Sweet-and-Spicy Roast Chicken **64**

Chicken Breasts with Garlic and Orange **65**

Pesto-and-Feta–Stuffed Chicken Breasts **66**

Crispy Pecan-Crusted Chicken Breasts **68**

Chicken Roulades with Prosciutto and Sage **69**

Chicken Kebabs with Lime and Pineapple **71**

Chicken with Black Bean Sauce **72**

Oven-Fried Chicken with Buttermilk Brine **73**

Braised Chicken Thighs with Tomatoes and Green Olives **74**

Hearty Chicken-Barley Stew **76**

Sweet Chipotle Drumsticks **77**

Tortellini with Chicken and Watercress **79**

Chicken-Chili Cobbler with Polenta **80**

Pasta with Chicken Sausage and Artichokes **81**

Coconut Turkey Fingers with Peach Sauce **82**

Pan-Glazed Turkey Tenderloin **84**

Spicy Blue Cheese Turkey Burgers **85**

Kielbasa with Cabbage and Caraway **86**

Duck with Cherry-Tarragon Glaze **87**

Sweet-and-Spicy Roast Chicken

PREP 10 min | **ROAST** 1 hr 15 min | **SERVES** 6 | **LEVEL** Intermediate

1 tablespoon packed light brown sugar

+

1 tablespoon paprika

+

1 tablespoon chipotle pepper sauce

+

1 tablespoon sherry vinegar

+

1 (3½-pound) whole chicken, giblets discarded

1 Preheat oven to 375°F. Spray roasting rack with nonstick spray and place in roasting pan.

2 Combine brown sugar, paprika, pepper sauce, vinegar, and ½ teaspoon salt in small bowl. With your fingers, gently separate chicken skin from breast meat and thigh meat of chicken; rub seasoning mixture onto meat under skin. Smooth skin back into place. Tuck wings under chicken and tie legs together with kitchen string. Place chicken on rack in roasting pan, breast side up. Roast chicken until instant-read thermometer inserted into thigh registers 165°F, 1¼–1½ hours.

3 Transfer chicken to cutting board; let stand 10 minutes. Discard skin and wings and carve chicken into 6 pieces.

PER SERVING (1 piece chicken): 82 g, 165 Cal, 4 g Total Fat, 1 g Sat Fat, 0 g Trans Fat, 89 mg Chol, 355 mg Sod, 3 g Total Carb, 2 g Total Sugar, 0 g Fib, 27 g Prot, 20 mg Calc.

4 PointsPlus® value

Per Serving

FYI **Rubbing seasoning under the skin of a bird is the best way to get flavorful results when you are discarding the skin before eating. An easy way to separate the skin from the breast meat is to slide 2 fingers between the meat and the skin and then gently loosen the skin by moving your fingers from side to side. Continue loosening the skin until you reach the thigh meat.**

Chicken Breasts with Garlic and Orange

PREP 10 min | **ROAST/BROIL** 35 min | **SERVES** 4 | **LEVEL** Intermediate

▲ **1 orange**

+

4 garlic cloves, minced

+

2 teaspoons olive oil

+

▲ **4 (7-ounce) bone-in, skin-on chicken breast halves**

1 Preheat oven to 350°F. Line baking sheet with foil and spray foil with nonstick spray.

2 Remove 2 teaspoons zest from orange. Combine zest, garlic, oil, ¾ teaspoon salt, and ½ teaspoon black pepper in small bowl. With your fingers, gently separate chicken skin from breast meat on one breast half; rub one fourth of garlic paste onto meat under skin. Smooth skin back into place. Place breast on baking sheet. Repeat with remaining chicken and garlic mixture. Cut orange into 8 slices and lay 2 slices over each breast.

3 Roast until chicken is cooked through, about 30 minutes. Preheat broiler; broil chicken 6 inches from heat until chicken and orange slices are browned, 3–4 minutes. Remove skin before eating.

PER SERVING (1 chicken breast half without skin):
112 g, 200 Cal, 6 g Total Fat, 1 g Sat Fat, 0 g Trans Fat, 89 mg Chol, 514 mg Sod, 1 g Total Carb, 0 g Total Sugar, 0 g Fib, 33 g Prot, 24 mg Calc.

5 PointsPlus® value
Per Serving

▲ Healthy Extra   **Roast some fresh asparagus alongside the chicken, on a separate baking sheet, to serve as an accompaniment.**

Pesto-and-Feta–Stuffed Chicken Breasts

PREP 15 min | **COOK** 15 min | **SERVES** 4 | **LEVEL** Intermediate

½ cup crumbled reduced-fat feta cheese

+

2 tablespoons pesto sauce

+

▲ 4 (5-ounce) skinless, boneless chicken breasts

+

1 teaspoon olive oil

+

3 tablespoons sliced fresh basil

1 To make stuffing, combine feta, pesto, and ¼ teaspoon black pepper in small bowl.

2 Make a pocket in side of each chicken breast by inserting sharp paring knife into thickest part and gently cutting back and forth until a small chamber opens; do not cut all the way through breast. Enlarge pockets gently with your fingers. Spoon about 2 tablespoons stuffing into each pocket. Close pockets with wooden toothpicks and sprinkle breasts with another ¼ teaspoon black pepper.

3 Heat oil in large nonstick skillet over medium heat. Add chicken and cook until browned and cooked through, 6–7 minutes per side. Remove toothpicks and sprinkle breasts with basil.

PER SERVING (1 stuffed chicken breast): 120 g, 236 Cal, 10 g Total Fat, 3 g Sat Fat, 0 g Trans Fat, 86 mg Chol, 371 mg Sod, 1 g Total Carb, 1 g Total Sugar, 1 g Fib, 33 g Prot, 87 mg Calc.

6 PointsPlus® value

Per Serving

Pesto-and-Feta–Stuffed Chicken Breasts

Crispy Pecan-Crusted Chicken Breasts

PREP 5 min | **COOK/BAKE** 15 min | **SERVES** 4 | **LEVEL** Basic

¾ **cup low-fat buttermilk**

+

▲ 4 **(5-ounce) skinless, boneless chicken breasts**

+

¼ **cup pecans, finely chopped**

+

⅓ **cup plain dried bread crumbs**

+

1 **teaspoon Cajun seasoning**

1 Pour buttermilk into medium bowl and add chicken; cover and refrigerate about 20 minutes.

2 Preheat oven to 350°F. Combine pecans, bread crumbs, and Cajun seasoning on sheet of wax paper. Remove 1 chicken breast from buttermilk, allowing excess buttermilk to drip off. Coat chicken with pecan mixture, gently pressing to help it adhere. Repeat with remaining chicken and pecan mixture. Discard any leftover buttermilk and pecan mixture. Lightly spray chicken on both sides with nonstick spray.

3 Spray large nonstick ovenproof skillet with nonstick spray and set over medium-high heat. Add chicken and cook until golden, 2–3 minutes per side. Transfer skillet to oven and bake until chicken is cooked through, 10–12 minutes.

PER SERVING (1 breast): 153 g, 252 Cal, 9 g Total Fat, 2 g Sat Fat, 0 g Trans Fat, 80 mg Chol, 317 mg Sod, 8 g Total Carb, 3 g Total Sugar, 1 g Fib, 32 g Prot, 84 mg Calc.

PointsPlus® value

Per Serving

FYI **Most skillets are ovenproof up to 350°F, but if you're not sure about yours, wrap the handle with a double thickness of foil. Alternatively, transfer the chicken to a small baking sheet before putting it in the oven and increase the baking time by a few minutes.**

Chicken Roulades with Prosciutto and Sage

PREP 15 min | **COOK** 15 min | **SERVES** 4 | **LEVEL** Intermediate

▲ **4 (5-ounce) skinless, boneless chicken breasts**

+

4 very thin slices prosciutto

+

12 sage leaves

+

Zest and juice of 1 lemon

+

▲ **1 cup reduced-sodium chicken broth**

1 Place 1 breast between 2 sheets of wax paper; gently pound with wooden mallet or rolling pin until meat is ½ inch thick. Top with slice of prosciutto and 3 sage leaves. Roll up chicken breast to enclose filling and secure with wooden toothpick. Repeat with remaining chicken breasts, prosciutto, and sage. Sprinkle roulades with ⅛ teaspoon salt and ¼ teaspoon black pepper.

2 Spray large nonstick skillet with nonstick spray and set over medium-high heat. Add roulades and cook, turning frequently, until lightly browned, about 5 minutes. Add broth, 1 tablespoon lemon zest, and 1 tablespoon lemon juice (reserve remaining zest and juice for another use); bring to boil. Reduce heat, cover, and simmer until chicken is cooked through, about 8 minutes. Remove toothpicks and serve chicken with sauce.

PER SERVING (1 roulade with ¼ cup sauce): 172 g, 195 Cal, 5 g Total Fat, 2 g Sat Fat, 0 g Trans Fat, 89 mg Chol, 534 mg Sod, 2 g Total Carb, 0 g Total Sugar, 0 g Fib, 34 g Prot, 19 mg Calc.

5 PointsPlus® value Per Serving

▲ Healthy Extra   **This juicy, savory chicken dish is excellent served with pasta (½ cup cooked whole wheat spaghetti or linguine per serving will increase the *PointsPlus* value by 2).**

Chicken Kebabs with Lime and Pineapple and Oven-Roasted Kale, page 167

Chicken Kebabs with Lime and Pineapple

PREP 15 min | **GRILL** 5 min | **SERVES** 4 | **LEVEL** Basic

Zest and juice of 1 lime

+

▲ **1 jalapeño pepper, seeded and minced**

+

2 garlic cloves, minced

+

▲ **1 pound skinless, boneless chicken breast**

+

▲ **1½ cups fresh pineapple chunks**

1 Combine lime juice, jalapeño, garlic, and ½ teaspoon salt in zip-close plastic bag. Cut chicken into 1½-inch chunks and add to bag. Squeeze out air and seal bag; turn to coat chicken. Refrigerate, turning bag occasionally, at least 10 minutes or up to 1 day.

2 Spray grill rack with nonstick spray; preheat grill to medium or prepare medium fire.

3 Remove chicken from marinade; discard marinade. Thread chicken and pineapple alternately on 4 metal skewers. Spray skewers with nonstick spray and place on grill rack; grill, turning frequently, until chicken is cooked through, about 7 minutes. Sprinkle skewers with lime zest.

PER SERVING (1 skewer): 153 g, 161 Cal, 3 g Total Fat, 1 g Sat Fat, 0 g Trans Fat, 63 mg Chol, 347 mg Sod, 10 g Total Carb, 6 g Total Sugar, 1 g Fib, 23 g Prot, 26 mg Calc.

4 PointsPlus® value Per Serving

FYI **You can substitute drained canned unsweetened pineapple chunks for the fresh pineapple with no change in the *PointsPlus* value.**

Chicken with Black Bean Sauce

PREP 10 min | **COOK** 15 min | **SERVES** 4 | **LEVEL** Basic

4 teaspoons Asian (dark) sesame oil

+

▲ **1 pound skinless, boneless chicken breast, cut into strips**

+

1 tablespoon finely grated peeled fresh ginger

+

▲ **1 (1-pound) bunch asparagus, cut into 2-inch pieces**

+

3 tablespoons black bean sauce with garlic

1 Heat nonstick wok or large nonstick skillet over medium-high heat; when very hot, add 2 teaspoons oil. Sprinkle chicken with ¼ teaspoon salt and add to wok. Cook, stirring occasionally, until lightly browned and cooked through, about 5 minutes. Transfer to plate.

2 Heat remaining 2 teaspoons oil in wok. Add ginger and cook, stirring constantly, until fragrant, about 30 seconds. Add asparagus and 3 tablespoons water; cook, covered, until asparagus is crisp-tender, 4–5 minutes.

3 Stir in black bean sauce and add chicken. Cook, stirring, until chicken is heated through, about 2 minutes.

PER SERVING (1¼ cups): 207 g, 198 Cal, 8 g Total Fat, 2 g Sat Fat, 0 g Trans Fat, 63 mg Chol, 283 mg Sod, 6 g Total Carb, 2 g Total Sugar, 3 g Fib, 26 g Prot, 42 mg Calc.

PointsPlus value

Per Serving

▲ Healthy Extra   **This is an excellent dish to serve with brown rice (⅔ cup cooked brown rice per serving will increase the *PointsPlus* value by *3*).**

Oven-Fried Chicken with Buttermilk Brine

PREP 10 min | **BAKE** 35 min | **SERVES** 6 | **LEVEL** Basic

 1 cup low-fat buttermilk

+

 ¼ teaspoon cayenne

+

 6 (5-ounce) skinless bone-in chicken thighs

+

 ½ cup whole wheat panko (Japanese bread crumbs)

+

 2 teaspoons chopped fresh thyme

1 Combine buttermilk, cayenne, and ½ teaspoon salt in large zip-close plastic bag; add chicken. Squeeze out air and seal bag; turn to coat chicken. Refrigerate, turning bag occasionally, at least 20 minutes or up to 1 day.

2 Adjust racks to divide oven into thirds and preheat oven to 400°F. Spray nonstick baking sheet with nonstick spray.

3 Combine panko and thyme on sheet of wax paper. Drain chicken and discard marinade. Coat thighs one at a time in panko mixture, pressing to help it adhere all over. Lightly spray each thigh with nonstick spray and place bone side down on baking sheet.

4 Bake chicken in lower third of oven until browned and instant-read thermometer inserted into each thigh registers 165°F, about 35 minutes. Let stand 5 minutes before serving.

PER SERVING (1 chicken thigh): 124 g, 198 Cal, 8 g Total Fat, 3 g Sat Fat, 0 g Trans Fat, 73 mg Chol, 311 mg Sod, 7 g Total Carb, 2 g Total Sugar, 1 g Fib, 22 g Prot, 58 mg Calc.

▲ Healthy Extra   **You can bake some small scrubbed potatoes along with the chicken for an easy side dish (1 small [3-ounce] baked potato has a** *PointsPlus* **value of** *2).*

Braised Chicken Thighs
with Tomatoes and Green Olives

| PREP 10 min | COOK 15 min | SERVES 4 | LEVEL Basic |

4 (¼-pound) skinless, boneless chicken thighs

▲ **⅔ cup reduced-sodium chicken broth**

▲ **3 plum tomatoes, chopped**

▲ **1 onion, thinly sliced**

⅓ cup halved pitted green olives

1 Spray large nonstick skillet with nonstick spray and set over medium-high heat. Add chicken and cook until lightly browned, about 3 minutes per side.

2 Add broth, tomatoes, onion, and olives; bring to boil. Reduce heat and simmer, uncovered, until vegetables are tender and chicken is cooked through, about 6 minutes.

PER SERVING (1 chicken thigh with ½ cup sauce):
223 g, 222 Cal, 12 g Total Fat, 3 g Sat Fat, 0 g Trans Fat, 74 mg Chol, 415 mg Sod, 6 g Total Carb, 4 g Total Sugar, 2 g Fib, 22 g Prot, 37 mg Calc.

Simple Additions **For a spicier sauce, add a few pinches of red pepper flakes and a couple of whole or sliced garlic cloves along with the broth.**

Braised Chicken Thighs with Tomatoes and Green Olives

Hearty Chicken-Barley Stew

▲ **½ ounce dried porcini mushrooms**

+

▲ **3 leeks, white and light green parts only**

+

1 pound skinless, boneless chicken thighs, cut into ½-inch pieces

+

▲ **1 (32-ounce) carton reduced-sodium chicken broth**

+

▲ **½ cup pearl barley, rinsed**

1 Combine mushrooms and 1 cup boiling water in small bowl; soak 10 minutes. Drain, reserving cooking liquid in a cup. Coarsely chop mushrooms.

2 Halve leeks lengthwise and rinse well under cold running water, spreading layers to remove any sand or dirt. Thinly slice leeks; place in colander and rinse again. Drain well and set aside.

3 Spray large nonstick saucepan with nonstick spray and set over medium-high heat. Add chicken and cook, stirring occasionally, until browned, about 8 minutes. Add leeks and cook until softened, about 5 minutes. Add broth, barley, and mushrooms. Carefully pour in reserved mushroom liquid, leaving any grit in bottom of cup. Reduce heat and simmer, covered, until barley is tender, about 40 minutes.

PER SERVING (1¼ cups): **365 g, 214 Cal, 6 g Total Fat, 2 g Sat Fat, 0 g Trans Fat, 50 mg Chol, 408 mg Sod, 21 g Total Carb, 2 g Total Sugar, 4 g Fib, 19 g Prot, 51 mg Calc.**

5 PointsPlus® value

Per Serving

▲ Healthy Extra   **Want even more great veggies in this stew? Add 2 sliced carrots and a handful of grape tomatoes along with the broth.**

Sweet Chipotle Drumsticks

PREP 5 min | **GRILL** 15 min | **SERVES** 4 | **LEVEL** Basic

½ cup
honey-flavored
barbecue sauce

+

1½ teaspoons
minced chipotles
en adobo

+

▲ 8 (3-ounce)
skinless
chicken
drumsticks

+

¼ cup
chopped fresh
cilantro

1 Spray grill rack with nonstick spray; preheat grill to medium or prepare medium fire.

2 Combine barbecue sauce and chipotles en adobo in small bowl. Place chicken on grill rack and cook, turning occasionally, 10 minutes. Brush with barbecue sauce. Continue to cook, turning, until chicken is deeply glazed and cooked through, 5–6 minutes longer. Transfer to platter and sprinkle with cilantro.

PER SERVING (2 drumsticks): 135 g, 167 Cal, 3 g Total Fat, 1 g Sat Fat, 0 g Trans Fat, 73 mg Chol, 461 mg Sod, 13 g Total Carb, 11 g Total Sugar, 0 g Fib, 20 g Prot, 11 mg Calc.

FYI   To broil the chicken, place the drumsticks on a foil-lined baking sheet. Broil 6 inches from the heat, turning once or twice, until browned, about 12 minutes. Brush the chicken with the sauce. Broil, turning frequently, until the drumsticks are deeply glazed and cooked through, about 4 minutes longer.

Tortellini with Chicken and Watercress

Tortellini with Chicken and Watercress

PREP 5 min | **COOK** 15 min | **SERVES** 4 | **LEVEL** Basic

1 (9-ounce) package whole wheat cheese tortellini

+

▲ **2 bunches watercress, trimmed**

+

▲ **2 cups diced cooked chicken breast**

+

▲ **½ cup fat-free half-and-half**

+

1 tablespoon grated Parmesan cheese

1 Prepare tortellini according to package directions, omitting salt. Drain and keep warm.

2 Meanwhile, spray large nonstick skillet with nonstick spray and set over medium-high heat. Add watercress and cook, stirring occasionally, until wilted, 1–2 minutes. Add tortellini, chicken, half-and-half, Parmesan, and ¼ teaspoon black pepper. Cook, tossing, until heated through, about 2 minutes.

PER SERVING (1¼ cups): **223 g, 353 Cal, 10 g Total Fat, 3 g Sat Fat, 0 g Trans Fat, 100 mg Chol, 408 mg Sod, 30 g Total Carb, 4 g Total Sugar, 5 g Fib, 34 g Prot, 223 mg Calc.**

9 PointsPlus® value
Per Serving

▲ Healthy Extra **Add 1 cup drained bottled roasted red pepper strips (not oil-packed) along with the chicken.**

Chicken-Chili Cobbler with Polenta

PREP 10 min | **COOK/BAKE** 40 min | **SERVES** 6 | **LEVEL** Basic

▲ **2 bell peppers, assorted colors, chopped**

+

¾ pound fresh spicy chicken sausage, casings removed

+

▲ **2 (10-ounce) cans diced tomatoes with green chiles**

+

▲ **1 (15-ounce) can pinto beans, rinsed and drained**

+

▲ **1 (16-ounce) tube fat-free polenta**

1 Preheat oven to 375°F. Spray 2-quart baking dish with nonstick spray.

2 Spray large nonstick skillet with nonstick spray and set over medium-high heat. Add bell peppers and cook, stirring frequently, until softened, about 8 minutes. Add sausage and cook, breaking it apart with wooden spoon, until browned, 6–8 minutes. Stir in tomatoes and beans; bring to boil. Spoon mixture into baking dish.

3 Cut polenta into 12 (½-inch) slices; lay slices over chili mixture. Loosely cover with foil and bake until chili is bubbling and polenta is softened, about 20 minutes.

PER SERVING (scant 1 cup chili and 2 slices polenta): 336 g, 234 Cal, 4 g Total Fat, 1 g Sat Fat, 0 g Trans Fat, 44 mg Chol, 747 mg Sod, 33 g Total Carb, 6 g Total Sugar, 6 g Fib, 16 g Prot, 171 mg Calc.

FYI **You can find tubes of prepared polenta in either the deli section or the produce section of most large supermarkets.**

Pasta with Chicken Sausage and Artichokes

PREP 5 min | **COOK** 20 min | **SERVES** 6 | **LEVEL** Basic

▲ **1 (12-ounce) package whole wheat linguine**

+

¾ pound low-fat chicken sausage, sliced

+

3 garlic cloves, minced

+

▲ **1 (14-ounce) can water-packed artichoke hearts, drained**

+

1 (26-ounce) jar reduced-sodium marinara sauce

1 Cook linguine according to package directions, omitting salt.

2 Meanwhile, to make sauce, spray large nonstick skillet with nonstick spray and set over medium-high heat. Add sausage and cook, stirring frequently, until browned, about 5 minutes. Add garlic and cook 1 minute.

3 Quarter artichoke hearts if they are large; add to skillet along with marinara sauce. Reduce heat and simmer until flavors are blended, about 10 minutes. Serve over linguine.

PER SERVING (1 cup pasta and 1 cup sauce): **276 g, 357 Cal, 9 g Total Fat, 2 g Sat Fat, 0 g Trans Fat, 43 mg Chol, 663 mg Sod, 48 g Total Carb, 8 g Total Sugar, 10 g Fib, 21 g Prot, 52 mg Calc.**

9 PointsPlus® value Per Serving

▲ Healthy Extra **Topping each serving of pasta and sauce with ¼ cup shredded fat-free mozzarella cheese will increase the per-serving *PointsPlus* value by *1*.**

Coconut Turkey Fingers with Peach Sauce

PREP 10 min | **BAKE** 15 min | **SERVES** 4 | **LEVEL** Basic

½ cup
no-sugar-
added peach
preserves

1 teaspoon
curry powder

▲ 1 pound
skinless,
boneless
turkey breast

½ cup
sweetened
flaked coconut,
chopped

¼ cup whole
wheat panko
(Japanese
bread crumbs)

1 Preheat oven to 425°F. Spray baking sheet with nonstick spray.

2 To make sauce, combine ¼ cup preserves and ½ teaspoon curry powder in small bowl.

3 Cut turkey into 16 strips. Combine turkey, ¼ teaspoon salt, and remaining ¼ cup preserves and ½ teaspoon curry powder in medium bowl; toss to coat. Combine coconut and panko on sheet of wax paper. One at a time, coat turkey strips with coconut mixture, lightly spray with nonstick spray, and place on baking sheet. Bake until fingers are golden and cooked through, about 15 minutes. Serve with sauce.

PER SERVING (4 turkey fingers and 1 tablespoon sauce): 144 g, 270 Cal, 4 g Total Fat, 3 g Sat Fat, 0 g Trans Fat, 74 mg Chol, 228 mg Sod, 29 g Total Carb, 20 g Total Sugar, 2 g Fib, 28 g Prot, 14 mg Calc.

7 PointsPlus® value
Per Serving

FYI   **These turkey fingers make an excellent appetizer or hors d'oeuvre. You can thread each one on a small bamboo skewer to make for easy dipping.**

Coconut Turkey Fingers with Peach Sauce

Pan-Glazed Turkey Tenderloin

| **PREP** 5 min | **COOK** 15 min | **SERVES** 4 | **LEVEL** Basic |

¼ **cup**
no-sugar-
added apricot
preserves

+

▲ **⅓ cup**
reduced-sodium
chicken broth

+

1 **tablespoon**
honey mustard

+

1 **teaspoon**
chopped fresh
thyme

+

▲ 1 **(1-pound)**
piece turkey
tenderloin

1 Whisk together preserves, broth, mustard, and thyme in small bowl.

2 Spray large nonstick skillet with nonstick spray and set over medium-high heat. Sprinkle turkey with ¼ teaspoon salt and add to skillet; cook, turning occasionally, until browned, about 3 minutes. Add apricot mixture and bring to a boil. Reduce heat and simmer, covered, until cooked through, 10–15 minutes.

3 Transfer turkey to cutting board and cut into 8 slices. Serve with sauce.

PER SERVING (2 slices turkey and 2 tablespoons sauce): 155 g, 158 Cal, 2 g Total Fat, 0 g Sat Fat, 0 g Trans Fat, 45 mg Chol, 248 mg Sod, 8 g Total Carb, 6 g Total Sugar, 0 g Fib, 29 g Prot, 4 mg Calc.

▲ Healthy Extra **For the perfect side dish, drizzle steamed green beans with lemon juice and toss with a few pinches of ground cumin and a pinch of salt.**

Spicy Blue Cheese Turkey Burgers

PREP 10 min | **COOK** 10 min | **SERVES** 4 | **LEVEL** Basic

▲ **1 pound ground skinless turkey breast**

+

▲ **2 scallions, chopped**

+

3 tablespoons plain dried bread crumbs

+

2 tablespoons hot pepper sauce

+

¼ cup reduced-fat blue cheese dressing

1 Combine turkey, scallions, bread crumbs, pepper sauce, and ¼ teaspoon salt in medium bowl. Form mixture into 4 (½-inch-thick) patties.

2 Spray ridged grill pan with nonstick spray and set over medium heat. Place patties on pan and cook until instant-read thermometer inserted into side of each one registers 165°F, about 5 minutes per side. Serve burgers drizzled with dressing.

PER SERVING (1 burger and 1 tablespoon dressing):
150 g, 168 Cal, 3 g Total Fat, 0 g Sat Fat, 0 g Trans Fat, 45 mg Chol, 574 mg Sod, 8 g Total Carb, 2 g Total Sugar, 1 g Fib, 29 g Prot, 14 mg Calc.

4 PointsPlus® value™
Per Serving

▲ Healthy Extra   **Sandwich these juicy burgers between slices of reduced-calorie bread, along with lots of tomato slices and some shredded lettuce (2 slices reduced-calorie whole-grain bread per serving will increase the *PointsPlus* value by 3).**

Kielbasa with Cabbage and Caraway

PREP 5 min | **COOK** 25 min | **SERVES** 4 | **LEVEL** Basic

▲ **2 cups reduced-sodium sauerkraut, rinsed and drained**

▲ **1 onion, chopped**

½ cup dry white wine or reduced-sodium chicken broth

1 teaspoon caraway seeds

½ pound reduced-sodium, reduced-fat turkey kielbasa

1 Combine sauerkraut, onion, wine, caraway seeds, and ¼ teaspoon black pepper in Dutch oven; bring to boil.

2 Cut kielbasa into 1-inch slices. Add kielbasa to pot and simmer, covered, until kielbasa is heated through and flavors are blended, about 20 minutes.

PER SERVING (about 1¼ cups): 195 g, 163 Cal, 8 g Total Fat, 3 g Sat Fat, 0 g Trans Fat, 30 mg Chol, 710 mg Sod, 7 g Total Carb, 4 g Total Sugar, 3 g Fib, 10 g Prot, 35 mg Calc.

4 PointsPlus® value
Per Serving

▲ Healthy Extra   **Add 2 peeled, cored, and chopped apples along with the sauerkraut.**

Duck with Cherry-Tarragon Glaze

PREP 5 min | **COOK** 15 min | **SERVES** 4 | **LEVEL** Intermediate

4 (5-ounce) skinless, boneless duck breast halves, trimmed

+

2 shallots, finely chopped

+

⅓ cup red wine

+

⅓ cup no-sugar-added cherry preserves

+

2 teaspoons chopped fresh tarragon

1 Spray large nonstick skillet with nonstick spray and set over medium heat. Sprinkle duck with ¼ teaspoon of salt; add to skillet and cook until golden and cooked through, about 5 minutes per side. Transfer to plate and keep warm.

2 Add shallots to skillet and cook, stirring, until softened, about 2 minutes. Stir in wine, preserves, another ¼ teaspoon salt, and any juices that have accumulated on plate with duck. Increase heat to medium high and simmer, stirring occasionally, until mixture is reduced to ½ cup, about 2 minutes. Stir in tarragon.

3 Slice each breast half thinly on bias and drizzle with 2 tablespoons of glaze.

PER SERVING (1 breast half and 2 tablespoons glaze): 203 g, 256 Cal, 6 g Total Fat, 2 g Sat Fat, 0 g Trans Fat, 109 mg Chol, 229 mg Sod, 16 g Total Carb, 11 g Total Sugar, 0 g Fib, 29 g Prot, 13 mg Calc.

▲ Healthy Extra **This is an excellent dish to serve with a flavorful whole grain such as quinoa (⅔ cup cooked quinoa has a *PointsPlus* value of 3).**

FROM THE SEA

Fabulous Fish and Shellfish

Poached Salmon with Wasabi Mayonnaise **91**

Roast Salmon with Cilantro and Lime **92**

Honey-Glazed Arctic Char **93**

Pan-Grilled Tuna and Lemons over Arugula **94**

Baked Whole Sea Bass with Fennel **95**

Swordfish Steaks with Caramelized Onions **96**

Crispy Cornmeal-Coated Flounder **98**

Catfish Amandine **99**

Mahimahi with Coconut Curry Sauce **100**

Striped Bass with Warm Sherry Vinaigrette **101**

Pan-Fried Shrimp in Red Pepper Sauce **103**

Lobster Ravioli with Plum Tomato Sauce **104**

Mussels in Spicy Garlic Broth **105**

Scallop-Broccoli Stir-Fry **106**

Seafood Salad with Lemon and Orzo **109**

4

Poached Salmon with Wasabi Mayonnaise
and Wild Rice Pilaf with Raisins and Orange, page 159

Poached Salmon with Wasabi Mayonnaise

PREP 10 min | **POACH** 15 min | **SERVES** 6 | **LEVEL** Intermediate

▲ 1 large onion, sliced into rings

+

1½ pounds skin-on salmon fillet, in one piece

+

▲ 4 cups reduced-sodium vegetable broth

+

6 tablespoons fat-free mayonnaise

+

2 teaspoons wasabi paste or prepared horseradish

1 Place onion in bottom of large pot or Dutch oven. Place salmon, skin side down, on top of onion. Pour broth around fish, covering it completely (if necessary, add water so that fish is completely covered by liquid).

2 Set pot over medium heat and bring to boil. Reduce heat, cover, and simmer just until salmon is opaque in center, about 10 minutes. Remove pot from heat; let salmon cool in broth, uncovered, 20 minutes.

3 Carefully lift salmon with spatula and place skin side up on large plate. Peel off and discard skin; discard broth or save for another use. Cover salmon with plastic wrap and refrigerate at least 1 hour or up to 24 hours.

4 Meanwhile, whisk together mayonnaise and wasabi; cover and refrigerate. Cut salmon into 6 pieces, transfer pieces to plates and top each with dollop of wasabi mayonnaise.

PER SERVING (1 piece salmon and 1 tablespoon wasabi mayonnaise): 155 g, 219 Cal, 9 g Total Fat, 1 g Sat Fat, 0 g Trans Fat, 73 mg Chol, 290 mg Sod, 7 g Total Carb, 4 g Total Sugar, 1 g Fib, 26 g Prot, 37 mg Calc.

5 PointsPlus® value

Per Serving

FYI **Run your fingers gently over the surface of the raw salmon to feel for small bones embedded in the flesh; if you find any, pull them out with a pair of clean tweezers or needle-nose pliers.**

Roast Salmon with Cilantro and Lime

PREP 10 min | **ROAST** 15 min | **SERVES** 4 | **LEVEL** Basic

3 tablespoons finely chopped fresh cilantro

1 tablespoon lime juice

1 garlic clove, minced

4 (5-ounce) pieces salmon fillet

1½ tablespoons fat-free mayonnaise

1 Preheat oven to 400°F. Spray small baking sheet with nonstick spray.

2 Combine cilantro, lime juice, garlic, ¼ teaspoon salt, and ⅛ teaspoon black pepper in small bowl. Place salmon on baking sheet. Brush tops of fillets with mayonnaise; press cilantro mixture into mayonnaise so that it adheres. Roast salmon just until opaque in center, 13–14 minutes.

PER SERVING (1 salmon fillet): **137 g, 238 Cal, 11 g Total Fat, 2 g Sat Fat, 0 g Trans Fat, 90 mg Chol, 264 mg Sod, 2 g Total Carb, 1 g Total Sugar, 0 g Fib, 32 g Prot, 22 mg Calc.**

6 PointsPlus value
Per Serving

▲ Healthy Extra   **Your favorite fat-free salsa is an excellent accompaniment to this fish.**

Honey-Glazed Arctic Char

| **PREP** 5 min | **COOK** 10 min | **SERVES** 4 | **LEVEL** Basic |

2 tablespoons reduced-sodium soy sauce

+

1 tablespoon honey

+

1 tablespoon minced peeled fresh ginger

+

1 tablespoon lemon juice

+

▲ 4 (5-ounce) pieces arctic char fillet

1 Whisk together soy sauce, honey, ginger, and lemon juice in small bowl. Pour mixture into large zip-close plastic bag; add arctic char. Squeeze out air and seal bag; turn to coat fish. Refrigerate, turning bag occasionally, at least 20 minutes or up to 1 hour.

2 Spray large nonstick ridged grill pan or nonstick skillet with nonstick spray and set over medium heat. Remove fish from marinade; reserve marinade. Place fish on pan and cook 5 minutes. Turn, brush once with reserved marinade, and cook just until fish is opaque in center, about 5 minutes more. Discard any excess marinade.

PER SERVING (1 piece char): 160 g, 219 Cal, 9 g Total Fat, 2 g Sat Fat, 0 g Trans Fat, 69 mg Chol, 360 mg Sod, 6 g Total Carb, 5 g Total Sugar, 0 g Fib, 30 g Prot, 2 mg Calc.

6 PointsPlus® value

Per Serving

Simple Additions   **Chopped chives, parsley, or cilantro makes a delicious garnish for this sweet-and-savory dish.**

Pan-Grilled Tuna and Lemons over Arugula

PREP 5 min | **COOK** 5 min | **SERVES** 4 | **LEVEL** Basic

▲ **4 (5-ounce) tuna steaks**

+

2 lemons, halved

+

8 tablespoons fat-free Italian dressing

+

▲ **1 (8-ounce) bag baby arugula**

1 Brush tuna and lemons all over with 3 tablespoons of dressing. Spray ridged grill pan with nonstick spray and set over medium-high heat. When pan is very hot, add tuna and lemons, placing lemons cut side down. Cook until tuna is browned and barely pink in center, 2–3 minutes per side, and lemons are deeply browned on cut side, about 5 minutes.

2 Meanwhile, toss together arugula and remaining 5 tablespoons dressing in large bowl. Divide arugula among 4 plates. Top with tuna steaks and place a grilled lemon half on side of each plate.

PER SERVING (1 tuna steak, 2 cups arugula, and ½ lemon): 245 g, 234 Cal, 7 g Total Fat, 2 g Sat Fat, 0 g Trans Fat, 53 mg Chol, 386 mg Sod, 10 g Total Carb, 3 g Total Sugar, 4 g Fib, 34 g Prot, 143 mg Calc.

6 PointsPlus® value Per Serving

▲ Healthy Extra **Add 2 cups halved grape tomatoes and 4 thinly sliced scallions to the arugula just before tossing it with the dressing.**

Baked Whole Sea Bass with Fennel

PREP 10 min | BAKE 35 min | SERVES 4 | LEVEL Intermediate

▲ **2 (1½-pound) whole sea bass or branzini, cleaned, tails and heads intact**

+

▲ **1 small fennel bulb, including fronds, finely chopped**

+

4 sprigs fresh thyme or parsley

+

½ cup dry white wine

1 Preheat oven to 400°F. Spray 9 x 13-inch baking dish with nonstick spray.

2 Sprinkle insides and outsides of sea bass with ¼ teaspoon salt and ¼ teaspoon black pepper. Fill cavity of each fish with equal amounts of fennel and herbs; close each cavity, fastening with wooden toothpicks. Pour wine into baking dish and cover tightly with foil. Bake just until bass are opaque in center, 35–40 minutes.

3 Remove and discard toothpicks and herb sprigs. Gently loosen meat from sides of fish and divide among 4 plates. Spoon juices and fennel over fish and serve.

PER SERVING (½ sea bass with ¼ cup fennel and juices): 206 g, 199 Cal, 3 g Total Fat, 1 g Sat Fat, 0 g Trans Fat, 62 mg Chol, 278 mg Sod, 5 g Total Carb, 0 g Total Sugar, 2 g Fib, 28 g Prot, 46 mg Calc.

4 PointsPlus® value
Per Serving

▲ Healthy Extra **Serve the fish with steamed red potatoes to help soak up all the savory pan juices (1 small [3-ounce] potato has a *PointsPlus* value of 2).**

Swordfish Steaks with Caramelized Onions

PREP 10 min | **COOK** 30 min | **SERVES** 4 | **LEVEL** Intermediate

2 teaspoons olive oil

+

▲ 3 onions, thinly sliced

+

¼ cup apple cider

+

▲ 4 (5-ounce) swordfish steaks, ½-inch thick

+

1 tablespoon chopped fresh flat-leaf parsley

1 Heat oil in large nonstick skillet over medium heat. Add onions, ⅛ teaspoon salt, and ⅛ teaspoon black pepper; cook, stirring occasionally, until onions begin to brown, about 10 minutes. Add cider and cook, covered, stirring occasionally, until onions are browned and very soft, about 10 minutes longer. Transfer onion mixture to small bowl; cover and keep warm.

2 Sprinkle swordfish with ⅛ teaspoon salt and ⅛ teaspoon black pepper. Wipe out skillet and set over medium-high heat. Add swordfish and cook until lightly browned and opaque in center, about 3 minutes per side. Transfer steaks to plates; top each serving evenly with onions and sprinkle with parsley.

PER SERVING (1 swordfish steak and ⅓ cup onions): 232 g, 222 Cal, 8 g Total Fat, 2 g Sat Fat, 0 g Trans Fat, 52 mg Chol, 270 mg Sod, 11 g Total Carb, 8 g Total Sugar, 2 g Fib, 27 g Prot, 38 mg Calc.

PointsPlus® value
Per Serving

FYI **Swordfish skin is tough and inedible, so be sure to trim it from your steaks and discard it either before or after cooking.**

**Swordfish Steaks with Caramelized Onions
and Broccolini with Walnuts and Shallots, page 168**

Crispy Cornmeal-Coated Flounder

½ **cup all-purpose flour**

+

½ **cup low-fat buttermilk**

+

▲ ½ **cup cornmeal**

+

▲ 4 **(5-ounce) flounder fillets**

+

2 **teaspoons canola oil**

1 Put flour on sheet of wax paper, put buttermilk in shallow bowl, and put cornmeal and ½ teaspoon salt on another sheet of wax paper. One at a time, coat fillets in flour, dip both sides in buttermilk, and then coat all over with cornmeal. Repeat until all fillets are coated.

2 Heat 1 teaspoon oil in large nonstick skillet over medium-high heat. Add fillets and cook until golden on bottom, about 4 minutes. Carefully turn with large spatula; add remaining 1 teaspoon oil to pan, tilting pan so that oil flows underneath fillets. Cook until fillets are opaque in center, about 3 minutes longer.

PER SERVING (1 flounder fillet): 167 g, 278 Cal, 4 g Total Fat, 1 g Sat Fat, 0 g Trans Fat, 68 mg Chol, 426 mg Sod, 29 g Total Carb, 2 g Total Sugar, 1 g Fib, 28 g Prot, 56 mg Calc.

PointsPlus® value

Per Serving

▲ Healthy Extra **Steamed green beans drizzled with lemon juice are an excellent side for this Southern-style flounder.**

Catfish Amandine

PREP 5 min | **COOK** 15 min | **SERVES** 4 | **LEVEL** Basic

2 tablespoons sliced almonds

+

▲ **4 (¼-pound) skinless catfish fillets**

+

2 teaspoons unsalted butter

+

1 shallot, minced

+

1 tablespoon white-wine vinegar

1 Place almonds in large nonstick skillet over medium-low heat. Cook, stirring occasionally, until golden and fragrant, about 4 minutes. Transfer to small bowl.

2 Sprinkle fillets with ¼ teaspoon salt and ¼ teaspoon black pepper. Spray same skillet with nonstick spray and set over medium heat. Add fillets; cook until lightly browned and just opaque in center, 2–3 minutes per side. Transfer to platter.

3 Heat butter in same skillet over medium heat until melted. Add shallot and cook, stirring frequently, until softened, about 1 minute. Add vinegar and cook, scraping up any browned bits from bottom of pan, until liquid evaporates, about 30 seconds. Remove skillet from heat and stir in toasted almonds. Spoon mixture over fillets.

PER SERVING (1 catfish fillet and 1½ tablespoons almond mixture): 131 g, 220 Cal, 12 g Total Fat, 4 g Sat Fat, 0 g Trans Fat, 69 mg Chol, 214 mg Sod, 2 g Total Carb, 0 g Total Sugar, 0 g Fib, 24 g Prot, 12 mg Calc.

5 PointsPlus® value™ Per Serving

FYI **Garlic lovers may wish to substitute 3 or more cloves of sliced garlic for the shallot.**

Mahimahi with Coconut Curry Sauce

PREP 10 min | **BAKE** 20 min | **SERVES** 4 | **LEVEL** Basic

▲ **4 (5-ounce) pieces mahimahi fillet**

+

2 tablespoons fresh lime juice

+

2 teaspoons Thai red curry paste, or to taste

+

▲ **2 bell peppers, assorted colors, thinly sliced**

+

½ cup light coconut milk

1 Spray 8 x 12-inch glass baking dish with nonstick spray. Sprinkle fillets with ¼ teaspoon salt and add to dish. Whisk together lime juice and curry paste in small bowl; pour over fillets. Turn fillets to coat and refrigerate 20–30 minutes.

2 Preheat oven to 350°F. Scatter bell peppers over fillets and add coconut milk. Cover dish tightly with foil and bake just until fillets are opaque in center, about 20 minutes.

PER SERVING (1 mahimahi fillet with ½ cup peppers and sauce): 240 g, 166 Cal, 3 g Total Fat, 0 g Sat Fat, 0 g Trans Fat, 103 mg Chol, 368 mg Sod, 6 g Total Carb, 3 g Total Sugar, 2 g Fib, 27 g Prot, 30 mg Calc.

4 PointsPlus® value
Per Serving

▲ Healthy Extra   **This is an excellent dish to serve with steamed rice (⅔ cup cooked brown rice per serving will increase the *PointsPlus* value by *3*).**

Striped Bass with Warm Sherry Vinaigrette

PREP 5 min | **COOK** 15 min | **SERVES** 4 | **LEVEL** Basic

▲ **4 (5-ounce) skin-on striped bass fillets**

+

2 garlic cloves, minced

+

1 tablespoon sherry vinegar

+

▲ **¾ cup reduced-sodium vegetable broth**

+

2 teaspoons chopped fresh thyme

1 Spray large nonstick skillet with nonstick spray and set over medium-high heat. Sprinkle fillets with ¼ teaspoon salt and ¼ teaspoon black pepper. Add fillets to skillet, skin side down, and cook, shaking pan constantly for first 30 seconds to prevent sticking, until crispy, about 5 minutes. Turn and cook just until fillets are opaque in center, about 2 minutes. Place skin side down on platter.

2 To make dressing, heat same skillet over medium-high heat. Add garlic and cook, stirring, 1 minute. Add vinegar and boil until reduced to glaze, about 10 seconds. Add broth and thyme; bring to simmer, stirring to scrape up any browned bits from bottom of skillet. Simmer until liquid is reduced by half, about 5 minutes. Pour sauce over fillets. Discard skin before eating.

PER SERVING (1 striped bass fillet and 1½ tablespoons sauce): 165 g, 148 Cal, 4 g Total Fat, 1 g Sat Fat, 0 g Trans Fat, 117 mg Chol, 272 mg Sod, 1 g Total Carb, 0 g Total Sugar, 0 g Fib, 26 g Prot, 31 mg Calc.

4 PointsPlus® value
Per Serving

▲ Healthy Extra **Steamed carrots make a sweet, colorful side to serve with this dish.**

Pan-Fried Shrimp in Red Pepper Sauce

Pan-Fried Shrimp in Red Pepper Sauce

PREP 15 min | **COOK** 10 min | **SERVES** 4 | **LEVEL** Basic

▲ **1 (12-ounce) jar roasted red peppers (not oil-packed), rinsed and drained**

1¼ cups marinara sauce

1 teaspoon olive oil

▲ **1 pound large shrimp, peeled and deveined**

4 garlic cloves, sliced

1 Put peppers and marinara sauce in food processor or blender and puree.

2 Heat oil in large nonstick skillet over medium-high heat. Add shrimp and garlic; cook, stirring constantly, until shrimp are pink, 3–4 minutes. Add pepper mixture and ¼ teaspoon black pepper to skillet. Reduce heat and cook, stirring occasionally, until mixture is slightly thickened and flavors are blended, about 4 minutes.

PER SERVING (1 cup): 252 g, 168 Cal, 4 g Total Fat, 0 g Sat Fat, 0 g Trans Fat, 168 mg Chol, 576 mg Sod, 12 g Total Carb, 6 g Total Sugar, 4 g Fib, 20 g Prot, 89 mg Calc.

4 PointsPlus® value Per Serving

FYI   **Look for peeled and deveined shrimp at your supermarket or fish store; using them in this recipe will shave about 10 minutes off your prep time.**

Lobster Ravioli with Plum Tomato Sauce

PREP 15 min | **COOK** 15 min | **SERVES** 4 | **LEVEL** Basic

1 (9-ounce) package lobster ravioli

+

▲ **1 pound plum tomatoes (about 5), cored, seeded, and chopped**

+

▲ **2 tablespoons tomato paste**

+

2 garlic cloves, minced

+

3 tablespoons sliced fresh basil

1 Cook ravioli according to package directions. Drain and keep warm.

2 Meanwhile, combine tomatoes, tomato paste, garlic, ¼ teaspoon salt, and ¼ teaspoon black pepper in large nonstick saucepan. Cook over medium-high heat, stirring occasionally, just until tomatoes are tender, about 5 minutes.

3 Divide ravioli among 4 plates or bowls and top evenly with sauce and basil.

PER SERVING (about 4 ravioli and ½ cup sauce): 189 g, 196 Cal, 3 g Total Fat, 1 g Sat Fat, 0 g Trans Fat, 22 mg Chol, 325 mg Sod, 33 g Total Carb, 5 g Total Sugar, 3 g Fib, 9 g Prot, 21 mg Calc.

5 PointsPlus® value Per Serving

- - - - - - - - - - - - - - - - - - - -

FYI   **To quickly seed plum tomatoes, halve each crosswise and then use your fingers to dig out the seeds.**

Mussels in Spicy Garlic Broth

PREP 15 min | **COOK** 15 min | **SERVES** 4 | **LEVEL** Intermediate

▲ **1 red onion, chopped**

+

4 garlic cloves, minced

+

▲ **1½ cups canned no-salt-added diced tomatoes**

+

¼ teaspoon red pepper flakes

+

▲ **4 pounds mussels, scrubbed and debearded**

1 Spray large nonstick skillet with nonstick spray and set over medium heat. Add onion and garlic; cook, stirring occasionally, until softened, about 3 minutes. Add tomatoes, red pepper flakes, ¼ teaspoon salt, and ¼ cup water; bring to boil. Reduce heat, cover, and simmer 5 minutes.

2 Add mussels to skillet and stir gently. Cover and cook until mussels open, about 5 minutes, stirring gently once or twice. Discard any mussels that do not open. Divide mussels and broth among 4 bowls.

PER SERVING (2½ cups mussels and broth):
243 g, 124 Cal, 2 g Total Fat, 0 g Sat Fat, 0 g Trans Fat, 28 mg Chol, 443 mg Sod, 12 g Total Carb, 4 g Total Sugar, 1 g Fib, 13 g Prot, 53 mg Calc.

3 PointsPlus® value

Per Serving

▲ Healthy Extra   **This is an excellent dish to serve with your favorite pasta. We recommend linguine (¾ cup cooked whole wheat linguine per serving will increase the *PointsPlus* value by 3).**

Scallop-Broccoli Stir-Fry

PREP 10 min | **COOK** 15 min | **SERVES** 4 | **LEVEL** Basic

2 teaspoons canola oil

+

▲ **1½ pounds sea scallops**

+

▲ **Florets from 1 broccoli crown, halved if large**

+

1 tablespoon minced peeled fresh ginger

+

1½ tablespoons reduced-sodium soy sauce

1 Heat large deep nonstick skillet or nonstick wok over medium-high heat until drop of water sizzles on it. Add canola oil and swirl to coat skillet. Add scallops; sprinkle with ⅛ teaspoon black pepper and cook just until opaque in center, about 3 minutes per side. Transfer to plate.

2 Add broccoli to skillet and stir-fry just until bright green, 2–3 minutes. Add ginger and stir-fry 1 minute. Stir in ¼ cup water and cook, covered, until broccoli is crisp-tender, about 2 minutes. Stir in scallops and soy sauce; cook, uncovered, stirring frequently, until heated through, about 1 minute longer.

PER SERVING (about 1¼ cups): 332 g, 226 Cal, 4 g Total Fat, 0 g Sat Fat, 0 g Trans Fat, 56 mg Chol, 525 mg Sod, 15 g Total Carb, 3 g Total Sugar, 4 g Fib, 33 g Prot, 114 mg Calc.

▲ Healthy Extra   **To add more great veggie crunch to this dish, stir in 1 red bell pepper, cut into thin strips, and 1 can sliced water chestnuts, drained, along with the broccoli.**

Scallop-Broccoli Stir-Fry

Seafood Salad with Lemon and Orzo

Seafood Salad with Lemon and Orzo

PREP 10 min | **COOK** 20 min | **SERVES** 4 | **LEVEL** Basic

▲ ½ **cup whole wheat orzo**

+

3 teaspoons olive oil

+

▲ 1 **pound frozen seafood medley (shrimp, calamari, scallops, mussels, etc.)**

+

▲ 1 **small red onion, diced**

+

Zest and juice of ½ lemon

1 Cook orzo according to package directions, omitting salt. Drain and rinse under cold running water until cool. Drain well and toss with 1 teaspoon oil.

2 Bring large pot of water to boil. Add seafood and cook just until opaque in center, about 2 minutes. Drain and rinse under cold running water until cool. Drain again and transfer to large bowl. Add onion, lemon zest and juice, ¼ teaspoon salt, ⅛ teaspoon black pepper, orzo, and remaining 2 teaspoons oil; toss to coat.

PER SERVING (1¼ cups): 171 g, 274 Cal, 4 g Total Fat, 1 g Sat Fat, 0 g Trans Fat, 260 mg Chol, 766 mg Sod, 23 g Total Carb, 1 g Total Sugar, 5 g Fib, 36 g Prot, 7 mg Calc.

6 PointsPlus® value ™ Per Serving

- -

▲ Healthy Extra **Add 2 stalks thinly sliced celery and 1 cup halved grape tomatoes along with the onion.**

MEATLESS MAINS

Great Vegetarian Entrées

Spaghetti "Bolognese" **112**

Stuffed Portobello Mushrooms **114**

Tofu and Shiitake Stir-Fry **115**

Egg and Broccoli Strudel **117**

Vegetable-Cheese Frittata **118**

Vegetarian Avgolemono with Dill **119**

Smoky Greens and Beans with Polenta **120**

Red Lentil–and–Black Bean Masala **122**

Roasted Eggplant and Cauliflower Curry **123**

Eggplant–Goat Cheese Rolls **125**

Penne with Blue Cheese and Squash **126**

Beet Salad with Pecan-Cheese Wedges **127**

Two-Tomato French Bread Pizzas **128**

Spaghetti "Bolognese"

PREP 5 min | **COOK** 20 min | **SERVES** 4 | **LEVEL** Basic

▲ **½ pound whole wheat spaghetti**

+

▲ **½ ounce dried porcini mushrooms**

+

6 ounces frozen soy crumbles, thawed

+

1½ cups low-sodium marinara sauce

+

¼ cup fresh basil

1 Cook spaghetti according to package directions, omitting salt.

2 Meanwhile, put mushrooms in measuring cup and pour ¾ cup boiling water over them. Let stand 5 minutes to soften. With slotted spoon, remove mushrooms from liquid; reserve liquid. Coarsely chop mushrooms.

3 Spray medium nonstick saucepan with nonstick spray and set over medium-high heat. Add mushrooms and soy crumbles. Cook, stirring frequently, 1 minute. Stir in marinara sauce and pour in reserved mushroom liquid, making sure to leave any grit in bottom of cup. Bring to boil. Reduce heat and simmer 5 minutes.

4 Remove saucepan from heat and stir in spaghetti. Divide among four plates. Tear basil into large pieces and sprinkle evenly over top of each serving.

PER SERVING (about 1½ cups): **244 g, 399 Cal,** 3 g Total Fat, 0 g Sat Fat, 0 g Trans Fat, 0 mg Chol, 92 mg Sod, 62 g Total Carb, 11 g Total Sugar, 14 g Fib, 30 g Prot, 184 mg Calc.

9 PointsPlus® value

Per Serving

- -

▲ Healthy Extra **Steamed zucchini is excellent with this hearty pasta; you can either serve it on the side or toss it into the sauce along with the spaghetti. Or (for an extra *PointsPlus* value of *1*) sprinkle each portion of pasta with ¼ cup shredded fat-free mozzarella cheese.**

Spaghetti "Bolognese"

Stuffed Portobello Mushrooms

PREP 10 min | **BAKE** 15 min | **SERVES** 4 | **LEVEL** Basic

1 (8-ounce) package frozen vegetarian sausage patties, thawed

+

▲ 1 celery stalk, finely chopped

+

¼ cup whole wheat dried bread crumbs

+

▲ 1 large egg, beaten

+

▲ 4 (4-inch) portobello mushroom caps

1 Preheat oven to 425°F. Spray baking sheet with nonstick spray.

2 Crumble sausage patties. Combine sausage, celery, bread crumbs, and egg in medium bowl. Spoon sausage mixture evenly onto mushroom caps, mounding it slightly in center. Lightly spray tops with nonstick spray.

3 Transfer mushrooms to baking sheet and loosely cover with foil. Bake 10 minutes; uncover and bake until mushrooms are browned and cooked through, about 5 minutes longer.

PER SERVING (1 stuffed mushroom): 172 g, 152 Cal, 5 g Total Fat, 1 g Sat Fat, 0 g Trans Fat, 0 mg Chol, 512 mg Sod, 15 g Total Carb, 4 g Total Sugar, 5 g Fib, 15 g Prot, 60 mg Calc.

PointsPlus® value
Per Serving
4

Simple Additions   **You can stir 2 teaspoons fresh thyme or ¾ teaspoon dried thyme into the filling mixture for extra flavor, plus add a pinch or two of cayenne for a little heat.**

Tofu and Shiitake Stir-Fry

▲ **2 (3½-ounce) packages shiitake mushrooms**

+

3 teaspoons Asian (dark) sesame oil

+

▲ **1 (14-ounce) package extra-firm tofu, drained and cubed**

+

▲ **1 red onion, sliced**

+

¼ cup hoisin sauce

1 Remove and discard mushroom stems; slice caps.

2 Heat large deep nonstick skillet or nonstick wok over medium-high heat until drop of water sizzles on it. Add 1 teaspoon oil and swirl to coat skillet; add tofu and stir-fry until golden, 5–6 minutes. Transfer to medium bowl.

3 Add remaining 2 teaspoons oil to skillet and swirl to coat; add mushrooms and onion. Stir-fry until vegetables are lightly browned, 5–6 minutes. Add tofu and stir-fry until hot, about 1 minute. Add hoisin sauce and cook, stirring constantly, just until blended, about 10 seconds.

PER SERVING (¾ cup): 196 g, 192 Cal, 9 g Total Fat, 1 g Sat Fat, 0 g Trans Fat, 0 mg Chol, 261 mg Sod, 19 g Total Carb, 7 g Total Sugar, 3 g Fib, 10 g Prot, 201 mg Calc.

▲ Healthy Extra   **Quick-cooking brown rice can be ready in almost the same amount of time it takes to cook this speedy stir-fry (⅔ cup cooked brown rice per serving has a *PointsPlus* value of 3).**

Egg and Broccoli Strudel

Egg and Broccoli Strudel

PREP 15 min | **COOK/BAKE** 30 min | **SERVES** 6 | **LEVEL** Advanced

▲ **2 cups small broccoli florets**

+

10 (9 x 14-inch) sheets frozen phyllo dough, thawed

+

▲ **4 large eggs**

+

2 teaspoons olive oil

+

½ cup shredded reduced-fat Jarlsberg cheese

1 Preheat oven to 375°F. Spray baking sheet with nonstick spray.

2 Bring medium pot of water to boil. Add broccoli and cook until crisp-tender, 3–4 minutes. Drain and blot broccoli dry with paper towels.

3 Meanwhile, lay 1 phyllo sheet on work surface with a long side facing you. (Keep remaining phyllo covered with damp kitchen towel and plastic wrap to prevent it from drying out while you work.) Lightly spray phyllo with nonstick spray. Layer 9 more phyllo sheets on top of first one, lightly spraying each sheet with nonstick spray. Cover phyllo with plastic wrap.

4 Whisk eggs, ¼ teaspoon salt, and ¼ teaspoon pepper in medium bowl. Stir broccoli into egg mixture. Heat oil in medium nonstick skillet and set over medium heat. Add egg mixture and cook, stirring with rubber spatula, just until set, 1–2 minutes. Spoon broccoli mixture over phyllo, leaving 2-inch border on all sides. Top with cheese. Fold short sides of phyllo over filling; then gently roll up jelly-roll-style, being careful not to tear phyllo.

5 Place strudel seam side down on baking sheet and lightly spray with nonstick spray. Cut four 1-inch slits in top to allow steam to escape. Bake until filling is hot and phyllo is golden, about 20 minutes. Cool strudel on baking sheet 15 minutes. Cut into 6 slices; serve warm or at room temperature.

PER SERVING (1 slice of strudel): 101 g, 192 Cal, 9 g Total Fat, 3 g Sat Fat, 0 g Trans Fat, 148 mg Chol, 344 mg Sod, 19 g Total Carb, 0 g Total Sugar, 1 g Fib, 10 g Prot, 118 mg Calc.

5 PointsPlus® value
Per Serving

Vegetable-Cheese Frittata

PREP 10 min | **COOK/BROIL** 20 min | **SERVES** 6 | **LEVEL** Basic

▲ **8 large eggs**

+

1½ teaspoons olive oil

+

▲ **1 red onion, thinly sliced**

+

▲ **2 bell peppers, assorted colors, diced**

+

▲ **1 cup shredded fat-free mozzarella cheese**

1 Preheat broiler.

2 Separate 2 eggs and put whites in large bowl; discard yolks or reserve for another use. Add remaining 6 whole eggs to bowl along with ⅛ teaspoon salt and ¼ teaspoon black pepper. Whisk until combined. Set aside.

3 Heat oil in 10-inch ovenproof skillet over medium-high heat. Add onion and bell peppers; cook, stirring occasionally, until softened, about 6 minutes. Add eggs and cook, stirring occasionally, until they start to set, 2–3 minutes. Reduce heat to medium-low and cook without stirring until eggs are almost completely set, about 7 minutes longer.

4 Sprinkle frittata with mozzarella. Place skillet under broiler. Broil 5 inches from heat until cheese is melted and eggs are set, 1–2 minutes. Cut into 6 wedges.

PER SERVING (1 wedge): 140 g, 135 Cal, 6 g Total Fat, 2 g Sat Fat, 0 g Trans Fat, 218 mg Chol, 267 mg Sod, 7 g Total Carb, 2 g Total Sugar, 1 g Fib, 14 g Prot, 195 mg Calc.

4 PointsPlus® value
Per Serving

FYI **If you have leftovers, wrap them well in plastic wrap and refrigerate up to 3 days. A wedge makes an excellent sandwich filling.**

Vegetarian Avgolemono with Dill

PREP 5 min | **COOK** 20 min | **SERVES** 4 | **LEVEL** Basic

▲ **1 (32-ounce) carton reduced-sodium vegetable broth**

+

▲ **⅔ cup whole wheat orzo**

+

▲ **4 large eggs**

+

Juice of 1 lemon

+

2 tablespoons chopped fresh dill

1 Bring broth and 2 cups water to boil in large saucepan. Add orzo and return to boil. Reduce heat, cover, and simmer until orzo is tender, about 8 minutes.

2 Meanwhile, lightly beat eggs, lemon juice, and ¼ teaspoon black pepper in medium bowl.

3 Stir about 2 tablespoons of hot broth into egg mixture. Gradually pour egg mixture into simmering soup and cook, stirring constantly, until egg is cooked through and forms thin strands, about 2 minutes. Serve sprinkled with dill.

PER SERVING (1¾ cups): 303 g, 125 Cal, 5 g Total Fat, 2 g Sat Fat, 0 g Trans Fat, 215 mg Chol, 197 mg Sod, 12 g Total Carb, 2 g Total Sugar, 2 g Fib, 8 g Prot, 41 mg Calc.

3 PointsPlus® value™

Per Serving

FYI **Look for organic low-sodium vegetable broth at your supermarket; most organic brands have much less sodium (up to 50% less) than regular low-sodium vegetable broths.**

Smoky Greens and Beans with Polenta

| PREP 5 min | COOK 20 min | SERVES 4 | LEVEL Basic |

▲ **1 (14½-ounce) can Mexican-style stewed tomatoes**

+

½ teaspoon minced chipotles en adobo

+

▲ **1 (16-ounce) bag triple-washed sliced kale**

+

▲ **1 (15½-ounce) can no-salt-added kidney beans, rinsed and drained**

+

▲ **1 (16-ounce) tube fat-free polenta**

1 Bring tomatoes and chipotles en adobo to boil in Dutch oven over medium-high heat; boil 1 minute.

2 Add kale in batches, stirring until each batch wilts. Cover and cook 4 minutes. Stir in beans. Reduce heat to medium, cover, and cook until kale is tender and flavors are blended, 7–8 minutes.

3 Meanwhile, cut polenta into 12 slices. Spray large nonstick grill pan with nonstick spray and set over medium-high heat. Add polenta and lightly spray with nonstick spray. Grill until golden, 4–5 minutes per side. Serve with kale mixture.

PER SERVING (1⅓ cups stew and 3 slices polenta): 443 g, 278 Cal, 1 g Total Fat, 0 g Sat Fat, 0 g Trans Fat, 0 mg Chol, 870 mg Sod, 57 g Total Carb, 8 g Total Sugar, 14 g Fib, 14 g Prot, 393 mg Calc.

7 PointsPlus® value
Per Serving

- -

▲ Healthy Extra   **For more color and fiber, add 2 thinly sliced carrots to the stew along with the tomatoes.**

Smoky Greens and Beans with Polenta

Red Lentil–and–Black Bean Masala

PREP 5 min | **COOK** 30 min | **SERVES** 4 | **LEVEL** Basic

▲ ¾ **cup red lentils**

▲ **1 red onion, chopped**

▲ **1 (15½-ounce) can no-salt-added black beans, rinsed and drained**

2 teaspoons garam masala

¼ cup chopped fresh cilantro

1 Bring 3 cups water to boil in medium saucepan. Add lentils and cook just until tender, about 15 minutes; drain.

2 Spray medium saucepan with nonstick spray and set over medium heat. Add onion and 2 tablespoons water. Cook, stirring occasionally, until onion is tender and liquid is evaporated, about 5 minutes. Add lentils, black beans, and garam masala; cook until heated through, about 3 minutes. Remove from heat and stir in cilantro.

PER SERVING (about 1 cup): 262 g, 224 Cal, 1 g Total Fat, 0 g Sat Fat, 0 g Trans Fat, 0 mg Chol, 18 mg Sod, 39 g Total Carb, 2 g Total Sugar, 11 g Fib, 16 g Prot, 72 mg Calc.

5
PointsPlus®
value
Per Serving

FYI   **Garam masala, a mild, fragrant blend of ground spices, is used in many Indian dishes. It can be found in health food stores and in the spice aisle of most supermarkets. You can make a simple version yourself by combining ½ teaspoon each black pepper, cinnamon, ground cloves, and ground cardamom and ¼ teaspoon ground cumin.**

Roasted Eggplant and Cauliflower Curry

PREP 10 min | **ROAST/COOK** 35 min | **SERVES** 4 | **LEVEL** Basic

▲ **1 small eggplant, cut into 1½-inch cubes**

+

▲ **2 cups cauliflower florets**

+

1 (16-ounce) jar vegetarian curry simmer sauce

+

▲ **1 (15-ounce) can no-salt-added chickpeas, rinsed and drained**

+

3 tablespoons chopped fresh cilantro

1 Preheat oven to 425°F. Spray large rimmed baking sheet with nonstick spray.

2 Place eggplant and cauliflower on baking sheet. Lightly spray with nonstick spray and toss to coat. Roast, stirring once, until vegetables are browned and tender, 20–25 minutes.

3 Heat simmer sauce and chickpeas in large saucepan over medium heat. Add roasted vegetables and simmer, covered, stirring occasionally, until flavors are blended, about 10 minutes. Remove from heat; stir in cilantro.

PER SERVING (1 cup): 250 g, 221 Cal, 7 g Total Fat, 1 g Sat Fat, 0 g Trans Fat, 0 mg Chol, 428 mg Sod, 31 g Total Carb, 5 g Total Sugar, 9 g Fib, 10 g Prot, 71 mg Calc.

5 PointsPlus® value

Per Serving

FYI **Simmer sauce comes in a variety of flavors and is a convenient pantry staple for quick, delicious, Indian-style meals. We recommend mild or medium-hot curry simmer sauce for this dish, but use a fiery vindaloo-style simmer sauce if you prefer a spicier stew.**

Eggplant–Goat Cheese Rolls

Eggplant–Goat Cheese Rolls

PREP 10 min | **BROIL/MICROWAVE** 10 min | **SERVES** 4 | **LEVEL** Intermediate

▲ **1 (1-pound) eggplant, cut lengthwise into 8 slices**

+

▲ **½ (14-ounce) can water-packed artichoke hearts, drained**

+

2 ounces low-fat goat cheese, crumbled

+

4 tablespoons chopped fresh basil

+

▲ **1 (8-ounce) can garlic-and-onion tomato sauce**

1 Spray broiler rack with nonstick spray and preheat broiler.

2 Place eggplant in one layer on broiler rack; lightly spray with nonstick spray. Broil eggplant 5 inches from heat until lightly browned, 3–4 minutes. Transfer, broiled side down, to work surface and let cool slightly.

3 Meanwhile, to make filling, chop artichokes. Combine artichokes, goat cheese, 2 tablespoons basil, and ¼ teaspoon pepper in medium bowl.

4 Place one eighth of filling on a short end of each eggplant slice and roll up. Place rolls, seam side down, in shallow 1-quart microwavable dish. Top rolls with tomato sauce and sprinkle with remaining 2 tablespoons basil. Cover with wax paper and microwave on High 4 minutes. Uncover and microwave until rolls are heated through and sauce is bubbling, 2–3 minutes.

PER SERVING (2 rolls with ¼ cup sauce): 236 g, 93 Cal, 1 g Total Fat, 0 g Sat Fat, 0 g Trans Fat, 0 mg Chol, 745 mg Sod, 16 g Total Carb, 4 g Total Sugar, 6 g Fib, 6 g Prot, 55 mg Calc.

2 PointsPlus value

Per Serving

▲ Healthy Extra   **Round out this meal with a salad—try romaine and radicchio drizzled with balsamic vinegar—and a delicious whole grain like bulgur (½ cup cooked bulgur per serving will increase the *PointsPlus* value by *2*).**

Penne with Blue Cheese and Squash

▲ ½ **pound whole wheat penne**

▲ 1 (20-ounce) **package cut and peeled butternut squash**

3 **shallots, thinly sliced**

▲ 1 cup **low-sodium vegetable broth**

¼ **pound low-fat blue cheese, crumbled**

1 Cook penne according to package directions, omitting salt.

2 Meanwhile, spray large nonstick skillet with nonstick spray and set over medium-high heat. Cut squash into ¾-inch chunks and add to skillet. Cook, stirring occasionally, until squash begins to brown, about 6 minutes. Add shallots and cook, stirring occasionally, until tender, about 2 minutes. Add broth and bring to boil. Reduce heat, cover, and simmer until squash is fork-tender, about 6 minutes.

3 Combine penne, squash mixture, blue cheese, and ¼ teaspoon black pepper in large bowl; toss well to coat.

PER SERVING (about 1½ cups): 310 g, 378 Cal, 8 g Total Fat, 4 g Sat Fat, 0 g Trans Fat, 20 mg Chol, 313 mg Sod, 64 g Total Carb, 7 g Total Sugar, 8 g Fib, 18 g Prot, 302 mg Calc.

10 PointsPlus® value
Per Serving

Simple Additions **Garnish each serving with a mixture of chopped fresh flat-leaf parsley and sage.**

Beet Salad with Pecan-Cheese Wedges

PREP 10 min | **COOK** 5 min | **SERVES** 6 | **LEVEL** Basic

▲ **1 (15-ounce) can diced beets, drained**

+

2½ tablespoons fat-free balsamic dressing

+

▲ **1 (5-ounce) bag baby arugula**

+

2 tablespoons finely chopped pecans

+

6 low-fat garlic-and-herb cheese wedges (from 8¾-ounce package)

1 Combine beets and dressing in large bowl. Add arugula and toss to coat. Divide salad among 6 plates.

2 Spread pecans on sheet of wax paper. Working with one cheese wedge at a time, gently press pecans onto 2 long sides.

3 Set medium nonstick skillet over medium heat. Add cheese wedges and cook until nuts are browned, about 2 minutes per side. Divide cheese wedges among salads.

PER SERVING (1 cheese wedge and 1⅔ cups salad): 128 g, 87 Cal, 4 g Total Fat, 1 g Sat Fat, 0 g Trans Fat, 10 mg Chol, 464 mg Sod, 9 g Total Carb, 7 g Total Sugar, 2 g Fib, 4 g Prot, 110 mg Calc.

2 PointsPlus® value

Per Serving

▲ Healthy Extra   **For extra sweetness and crunch, add a cored diced apple to the salad along with the arugula.**

Two-Tomato French Bread Pizzas

PREP 10 min | **BROIL** 5 min | **SERVES** 4 | **LEVEL** Basic

1 (½-pound) loaf whole wheat French bread

+

½ cup part-skim ricotta cheese

+

2 tablespoons sun-dried-tomato pesto

+

▲ 1 yellow tomato, cut into thin wedges

+

¼ cup fresh basil, chopped

1 Preheat broiler.

2 Split bread horizontally; pull out soft center from each piece and discard, or reserve to make bread crumbs for another day. Mix ricotta and ¼ teaspoon black pepper in small bowl.

3 Spread each piece of bread with 1 tablespoon pesto. Top each piece with half of tomatoes wedges and ¼ cup ricotta mixture. Broil pizzas 6 inches from heat until ricotta is hot, 5–6 minutes. Sprinkle evenly with basil. Cut each piece in half crosswise, making 4 pizzas.

PER SERVING (1 pizza): 151 g, 228 Cal, 6 g Total Fat, 2 g Sat Fat, 0 g Trans Fat, 10 mg Chol, 406 mg Sod, 33 g Total Carb, 3 g Total Sugar, 4 g Fib, 11 g Prot, 108 mg Calc.

6 PointsPlus® value
Per Serving

▲ Healthy Extra **If you have access to particularly flavorful tomatoes, use two instead of one to top these crunchy pizzas.**

Two-Tomato French Bread Pizzas

READY IN 20 MINUTES OR LESS

Easy Weeknight Wonders

Ginger-Sesame Steak Kebabs **132**

Rosemary-Balsamic Pork Chops **133**

Grilled Pork and Veggie Skewers **135**

Mediterranean Lamb Chops **136**

Chicken Cutlets with Lemon-Caper Sauce **137**

Quick Chicken and Black Bean Burritos **138**

Grilled Turkey with Plums and Greens **141**

Tuna Teriyaki Burgers **142**

Souvlaki-Style Fish Kebabs **143**

Catfish Po' Boys **144**

Lemon-Cumin Halibut Steaks **146**

Beer-Braised Mussels **147**

Lime-and-Chili–Grilled Shrimp **148**

Spinach and Sun-Dried Tomato Pizza **149**

Fried Rice with Snow Peas **151**

Ginger-Sesame Steak Kebabs

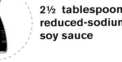

2½ **tablespoons reduced-sodium soy sauce**

+

2½ **tablespoons red-wine vinegar**

+

1 **tablespoon minced peeled fresh ginger**

+

½ **teaspoon Asian (dark) sesame oil**

+

▲ 1 **pound boneless sirloin steak, trimmed**

1 Spray broiler rack with nonstick spray and preheat boiler.

2 Combine soy sauce, vinegar, ginger, and sesame oil in small bowl.

3 Cut steak into 1-inch cubes. Thread on 8 (10-inch) metal skewers; brush with half of soy sauce mixture. Broil kebabs 5 inches from heat 4 minutes. Turn and brush with remaining soy sauce mixture; continue to grill until medium rare, about 4 minutes longer.

PER SERVING (2 skewers): 107 g, 170 Cal, 6 g Total Fat, 2 g Sat Fat, 0 g Trans Fat, 49 mg Chol, 389 mg Sod, 1 g Total Carb, 0 g Total Sugar, 0 g Fib, 27 g Prot, 20 mg Calc.

FYI **Instead of peeling and mincing the ginger, save a few minutes of prep time by simply grating it (skin and all) on the small holes of a box grater or with a Microplane grater.**

Rosemary-Balsamic Pork Chops

PREP 5 min | **COOK** 15 min | **SERVES** 4 | **LEVEL** Basic

▲ **4 (5-ounce) bone-in pork loin chops, about ½-inch thick, trimmed**

+

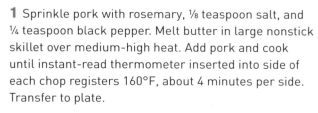

2 teaspoons chopped fresh rosemary

+

1 tablespoon unsalted butter

+

▲ **¾ cup low-sodium chicken broth**

+

3 tablespoons balsamic vinegar

1 Sprinkle pork with rosemary, ⅛ teaspoon salt, and ¼ teaspoon black pepper. Melt butter in large nonstick skillet over medium-high heat. Add pork and cook until instant-read thermometer inserted into side of each chop registers 160°F, about 4 minutes per side. Transfer to plate.

2 Add broth and vinegar to skillet; bring to boil, scraping up browned bits from bottom of pan. Boil until mixture is syrupy, about 5 minutes. Add pork and cook until heated through, about 1 minute per side.

PER SERVING (1 pork chop with 1 tablespoon sauce):
131 g, 170 Cal, 8 g Total Fat, 3 g Sat Fat, 0 g Trans Fat, 67 mg Chol, 129 mg Sod, 3 g Total Carb, 2 g Total Sugar, 0 g Fib, 20 g Prot, 24 mg Calc.

4 PointsPlus® value Per Serving

▲ Healthy Extra   **Round out your meal with two quick-cooking sides: whole wheat couscous (⅔ cup per serving will increase the *PointsPlus* value by 3) and steamed asparagus.**

Grilled Pork and Veggie Skewers

Grilled Pork and Veggie Skewers

PREP 10 min | **GRILL** 5 min | **SERVES** 4 | **LEVEL** Basic

▲ **1 pound pork tenderloin, trimmed**

+

▲ **2 zucchini**

+

▲ **2 plum tomatoes**

+

▲ **12 cremini or white mushrooms**

+

1½ teaspoons Italian seasoning

1 Spray grill rack with nonstick spray. Preheat grill to medium-high or prepare medium-hot fire.

2 Cut pork into 1½-inch cubes, cut zucchini into 1½-inch pieces, and quarter each tomato. Thread pork, mushrooms, zucchini, and tomatoes alternately on 4 (12-inch) metal skewers; sprinkle evenly with Italian seasoning and ½ teaspoon salt. Spray kebabs with nonstick spray.

3 Place kebabs on grill rack and grill, turning every 2 minutes, until cooked through, 6–7 minutes.

PER SERVING (1 skewer): 276 g, 160 Cal, 3 g Total Fat, 1 g Sat Fat, 0 g Trans Fat, 62 mg Chol, 354 mg Sod, 7 g Total Carb, 4 g Total Sugar, 2 g Fib, 25 g Prot, 34 mg Calc.

4 PointsPlus® value
Per Serving

FYI   **You can also use 4 (12-inch) wooden skewers in this recipe. To make sure they won't burn on the grill, soak them in water for at least 15 minutes before assembling the kebabs.**

Mediterranean Lamb Chops

PREP 5 min | **COOK** 10 min | **SERVES** 4 | **LEVEL** Basic

2 garlic cloves

+

1 teaspoon fennel seeds

+

1 tablespoon chopped fresh flat-leaf parsley

+

▲ 4 (5-ounce) boneless lamb loin chops, about ¾-inch thick, trimmed

+

1 teaspoon olive oil

1 Crush garlic through press and crush fennel seeds with bottom of heavy saucepan. Transfer garlic and fennel seeds to cup; stir in parsley, ¼ teaspoon salt, and ¼ teaspoon black pepper. Rub garlic mixture over lamb.

2 Heat oil in large nonstick skillet over medium-high heat. Add lamb and cook until instant-read thermometer inserted into side of each chop registers 145°F for medium, about 4 minutes per side.

PER SERVING (1 lamb chop): 84 g, 173 Cal, 8 g Total Fat, 3 g Sat Fat, 0 g Trans Fat, 91 mg Chol, 190 mg Sod, 1 g Total Carb, 0 g Total Sugar, 0 g Fib, 24 g Prot, 27 mg Calc.

▲ Healthy Extra   **Accompany these succulent chops with steamed sugar snap peas and lemon wedges.**

Chicken Cutlets with Lemon-Caper Sauce

PREP 5 min | **COOK** 10 min | **SERVES** 4 | **LEVEL** Basic

**4 teaspoons
unsalted butter**

+

▲ **4 (¼-pound)
thin-sliced
skinless,
boneless
chicken cutlets**

+

**Zest and juice
of 1 lemon**

+

▲ **⅓ cup
reduced-sodium
chicken broth**

+

**2 tablespoons
capers, drained**

1 Melt 2 teaspoons butter in large nonstick skillet over medium-high heat. Add chicken and cook until lightly browned, about 2 minutes per side.

2 Stir lemon zest and juice, broth, capers, and ¼ teaspoon black pepper into skillet; bring to boil. Reduce heat and simmer until chicken is cooked through, about 2 minutes, turning cutlets halfway through cooking time.

3 Transfer chicken to platter. Remove skillet from heat; whisk in remaining 2 teaspoons butter. Pour sauce over chicken.

PER SERVING (1 chicken cutlet and 2 tablespoons sauce):
118 g, 163 Cal, 7 g Total Fat, 3 g Sat Fat, 0 g Trans Fat, 73 mg Chol, 229 mg Sod, 2 g Total Carb, 0 g Total Sugar, 1 g Fib, 23 g Prot, 21 mg Calc.

PointsPlus®
value

Per Serving

Simple Additions   **Chopped parsley makes a quick and classic garnish for this dish, but you can use just about any mild leafy herb—dill, basil, or chervil would be delicious as well.**

Quick Chicken and Black Bean Burritos

| PREP 5 min | COOK 10 min | SERVES 4 | LEVEL Basic |

▲ ¾ pound ground skinless chicken breast

▲ 1 (15½-ounce) can no-salt-added black beans, rinsed and drained

4 (7-inch) flour tortillas

▲ 8 tablespoons fat-free salsa

4 tablespoons shredded low-fat Mexican cheese blend

1 Spray large nonstick skillet with nonstick spray and set over medium-high heat. Add chicken and cook, breaking it apart with wooden spoon, until browned, about 6 minutes. Add beans and cook, stirring occasionally, until heated through, about 2 minutes.

2 Meanwhile, warm tortillas according to package directions.

3 Place 1 tortilla on work surface and spoon one quarter of chicken mixture down center. Top with 2 tablespoons salsa and 1 tablespoon shredded cheese. Fold sides of tortilla over filling and roll up. Repeat with remaining tortillas, chicken mixture, salsa, and cheese.

PER SERVING (1 burrito): 248 g, 350 Cal, 7 g Total Fat, 2 g Sat Fat, 0 g Trans Fat, 51 mg Chol, 521 mg Sod, 41 g Total Carb, 2 g Total Sugar, 7 g Fib, 29 g Prot, 218 mg Calc.

▲ Healthy Extra   **Round out your burritos with thinly sliced leaf lettuce and diced tomatoes and cilantro.**

Quick Chicken and Black Bean Burritos

Grilled Turkey with Plums and Greens

Grilled Turkey with Plums and Greens

PREP 10 min | **COOK** 5 min | **SERVES** 4 | **LEVEL** Basic

▲ **4 (¼-pound) turkey breast cutlets**

+

▲ **4 small plums, cut into thin wedges**

+

▲ **½ English cucumber, sliced**

+

▲ **1 (5-ounce) container frisée-blend salad greens**

+

⅓ cup fat-free raspberry vinaigrette

1 Spray nonstick ridged grill pan with nonstick spray and set over medium-high heat. Sprinkle cutlets with ¼ teaspoon salt and ¼ teaspoon black pepper; spray both sides with nonstick spray. Place cutlets on pan and cook until cooked through, about 2 minutes per side. Transfer to cutting board and let cool 2 minutes.

2 Slice turkey crosswise into strips and transfer to large bowl. Add plums, cucumber, greens, and dressing; toss to coat. Divide among 4 plates.

PER SERVING (2½ cups): **276 g, 185 Cal, 1 g Total Fat, 0 g Sat Fat, 0 g Trans Fat, 45 mg Chol, 269 mg Sod, 15 g Total Carb, 10 g Total Sugar, 2 g Fib, 29 g Prot, 19 mg Calc.**

4
PointsPlus®
value
Per Serving

▲ Healthy Extra   **Sweeten your salad by garnishing it with 6 ounces of fresh raspberries.**

Tuna Teriyaki Burgers

PREP 10 min	COOK 10 min	SERVES 4	LEVEL Intermediate

▲ **1 pound tuna steak**

+

3 tablespoons chopped fresh cilantro

+

1 tablespoon Dijon mustard

+

2 teaspoons teriyaki sauce

+

1 teaspoon grated peeled fresh ginger

1 Cut tuna into 2-inch pieces; put pieces in food processor and pulse until finely chopped.

2 Put tuna, cilantro, mustard, teriyaki sauce, ginger, and ½ teaspoon black pepper in large bowl; stir just until blended. Form into 4 (¾-inch-thick) burgers.

3 Spray nonstick skillet with nonstick spray and set over medium heat. Add burgers and cook about 4 minutes per side for medium or until desired degree of doneness.

PER SERVING (1 burger): **121 g, 215 Cal, 7 g Total Fat, 2 g Sat Fat, 0 g Trans Fat, 56 mg Chol, 190 mg Sod, 1 g Total Carb, 0 g Total Sugar, 0 g Fib, 34 g Prot, 12 mg Calc.**

▲ Healthy Extra **Serve these deliciously meaty burgers over a bed of watercress sprigs tossed with sliced red bell pepper and lime juice.**

Souvlaki-Style Fish Kebabs

PREP 10 min | **COOK** 5 min | **SERVES** 4 | **LEVEL** Basic

4 garlic cloves, minced

+

2 teaspoons chopped fresh oregano

+

2 teaspoons chopped fresh thyme

+

Zest and juice of 1 lemon

+

▲ 1 pound swordfish, skin and any dark red spots cut away

1 Combine garlic, oregano, thyme, and 2 tablespoons lemon juice in medium bowl (reserve remaining juice for another use). Cut swordfish into 1-inch cubes and add to bowl along with ½ teaspoon salt and ½ teaspoon black pepper; toss to combine.

2 Spray ridged grill pan or nonstick skillet with nonstick spray and set over medium heat. When pan is hot, thread fish on 4 (12-inch) metal skewers. Spray kebabs lightly with nonstick spray. Place on pan and cook just until opaque in center, turning occasionally, about 6 minutes. Serve sprinkled with lemon zest.

PER SERVING (1 kebab): 98 g, 139 Cal, 4 g Total Fat, 1 g Sat Fat, 0 g Trans Fat, 41 mg Chol, 387 mg Sod, 3 g Total Carb, 0 g Total Sugar, 1 g Fib, 21 g Prot, 25 mg Calc.

PointsPlus® value
Per Serving

FYI **Most other firm, thick, skinless fish fillets will work in this recipe, including Arctic char and cod.**

Catfish Po' Boys

| **PREP** 10 min | **COOK** 5 min | **SERVES** 4 | **LEVEL** Basic |

▲ **4 (5-ounce) skinless catfish fillets**

✚

1½ teaspoons Cajun seasoning

✚

▲ **1⅓ cups shredded romaine lettuce**

✚

6 tablespoons fat-free tartar sauce

✚

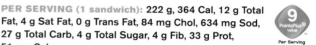

4 multigrain hamburger buns, toasted

1 Sprinkle catfish evenly with Cajun seasoning. Spray ridged grill pan with nonstick spray and set over medium-high heat. Place catfish on pan and cook just until opaque in center, 2–3 minutes per side.

2 Layer ⅓ cup romaine, 1 catfish fillet, and 1½ tablespoons tartar sauce on each bun.

PER SERVING (1 sandwich): 222 g, 364 Cal, 12 g Total Fat, 4 g Sat Fat, 0 g Trans Fat, 84 mg Chol, 634 mg Sod, 27 g Total Carb, 4 g Total Sugar, 4 g Fib, 33 g Prot, 51 mg Calc.

9 PointsPlus® value
Per Serving

▲ Healthy Extra   **Serve these po' boys with a platter of other classic accompaniments so everyone can customize their sandwich: sliced tomato, unsweetened dill pickle slices, sliced red onion, lemon wedges, and roasted bell peppers (not packed in oil).**

Catfish Po' Boys

Lemon-Cumin Halibut Steaks

PREP 5 min | **COOK** 10 min | **SERVES** 4 | **LEVEL** Basic

1 lemon

+

2 garlic cloves, minced

+

2 teaspoons olive oil

+

1 teaspoon ground cumin

+

▲ 4 (6-ounce) halibut steaks

1 Halve lemon; grate zest and squeeze juice from one half; reserve remaining half for garnish.

2 Combine lemon zest and juice, garlic, oil, cumin, ½ teaspoon salt, and ¼ teaspoon black pepper in small bowl. Brush the mixture evenly over both sides of halibut steaks.

3 Spray nonstick ridged grill pan with nonstick spray and set over medium-high heat. Cook halibut just until opaque in center, about 4 minutes per side. Cut remaining lemon half into 4 wedges and serve with halibut.

PER SERVING (1 halibut steak and 1 lemon wedge): 190 g, 218 Cal, 7 g Total Fat, 1 g Sat Fat, 0 g Trans Fat, 54 mg Chol, 384 mg Sod, 2 g Total Carb, 0 g Total Sugar, 1 g Fib, 36 g Prot, 92 mg Calc.

5 PointsPlus® value™

Per Serving

▲ Healthy Extra **Round out your meal with potatoes and steamed broccoli (1 cooked 3-ounce red potato and 1 cup steamed broccoli florets per serving will increase the *PointsPlus* value by 2).**

Beer-Braised Mussels

PREP 10 min | **COOK** 10 min | **SERVES** 4 | **LEVEL** Intermediate

1 (12-ounce) can light beer

+

▲ **1 (14½-ounce) can diced tomatoes with roasted garlic**

+

▲ **4 pounds small mussels, scrubbed and debearded**

+

¼ cup fresh flat-leaf parsley, chopped

+

4 (1-ounce) pieces whole wheat French bread

1 Bring beer to boil in large Dutch oven. Stir in tomatoes and add mussels. Cover and return to boil. Reduce heat and simmer, covered, until mussels open, 6–8 minutes.

2 With slotted spoon, divide mussels and tomatoes among 4 large bowls. Discard any mussels that do not open. Stir parsley into broth; ladle broth evenly over each serving. Serve with bread.

PER SERVING (16 mussels, ¾ cup broth, and 1 slice bread): 308 g, 198 Cal, 3 g Total Fat, 0 g Sat Fat, 0 g Trans Fat, 24 mg Chol, 577 mg Sod, 24 g Total Carb, 4 g Total Sugar, 2 g Fib, 14 g Prot, 46 mg Calc.

6 PointsPlus© value
Per Serving

FYI   Sometimes you'll find long hairlike strands protruding from a mussel's shell. These are known as "beards," and it's usual (although not absolutely necessary) to remove them before cooking. To do so, hold the mussel gently in one hand and use a small paring knife to scrape off the beard.

Lime-and-Chili–Grilled Shrimp

| **PREP** 10 min | **GRILL** 5 min | **SERVES** 4 | **LEVEL** Basic |

Zest and juice of 1 lime

+

▲ **1 jalapeño pepper, seeded and chopped**

+

2 teaspoons chili powder

+

½ teaspoon ground cumin

+

▲ **1½ pounds large shrimp, in the shells**

1 Combine lime zest and juice, jalapeño, chili powder, cumin, and ¼ teaspoon salt in large bowl. Add shrimp and toss to coat. Cover and refrigerate 30 minutes.

2 Spray grill rack with nonstick spray; prepare grill for medium-hot cooking. Thread 4–5 shrimp on each of 4 metal skewers. Place skewers on grill rack and grill just until shrimp are opaque in center, about 2 minutes per side.

PER SERVING (1 skewer): 144 g, 138 Cal, 2 g Total Fat, 0 g Sat Fat, 0 g Trans Fat, 252 mg Chol, 449 mg Sod, 2 g Total Carb, 0 g Total Sugar, 1 g Fib, 27 g Prot, 60 mg Calc.

3 PointsPlus® value
Per Serving

▲ Healthy Extra   **When you skewer the shrimp, you can alternate each shrimp with a chunk of a grill-friendly fruit: Pineapple, peaches, and apricots are good choices.**

Spinach and Sun-Dried Tomato Pizza

PREP 5 min | **MICROWAVE/BROIL** 5 min | **SERVES** 6 | **LEVEL** Basic

 1 (8-ounce) microwavable bag fresh spinach

⅓ cup oil-packed sun-dried tomatoes, drained and rinsed

1 (10-ounce) prebaked thin whole wheat pizza crust

½ cup shredded low-fat Italian cheese blend

½ cup crumbled low-fat goat cheese

1 Preheat broiler. Microwave spinach according to package directions.

2 Meanwhile, chop sun-dried tomatoes. Transfer spinach to cutting board and let cool slightly, about 3 minutes. Coarsely chop spinach; transfer to medium bowl and stir in sun-dried tomatoes.

3 Place pizza crust on pizza pan or baking sheet. Broil crust 5 inches from heat until golden, 30–60 seconds per side. Remove crust from broiler; spread top with spinach mixture, leaving 1-inch border. Sprinkle cheese blend and goat cheese evenly over spinach. Broil until cheeses melt, about 1 minute. Cut into 6 wedges.

PER SERVING (1 wedge): 110 g, 168 Cal, 5 g Total Fat, 1 g Sat Fat, 0 g Trans Fat, 5 mg Chol, 452 mg Sod, 23 g Total Carb, 0 g Total Sugar, 4 g Fib, 9 g Prot, 150 mg Calc.

- - -

FYI **Want to use baby spinach in this recipe? Combine 7 cups spinach and 1 tablespoon water in a large nonstick skillet. Set the skillet over medium-high heat and cook, stirring constantly, just until the spinach is wilted, about 2 minutes.**

Fried Rice with Snow Peas

Fried Rice with Snow Peas

PREP 10 min | **COOK** 10 min | **SERVES** 4 | **LEVEL** Basic

▲ **2 cups instant brown rice**

+

▲ **4 large eggs**

+

2 tablespoons reduced-sodium soy sauce

+

▲ **½ pound fresh snow peas**

+

▲ **1 red bell pepper, thinly sliced**

1 Cook rice according to package directions, omitting salt.

2 Meanwhile, whisk together eggs and soy sauce in small bowl.

3 Spray large nonstick skillet with nonstick spray and set over medium-high heat. Add snow peas and bell pepper; cook, stirring frequently, until vegetables are crisp-tender, about 4 minutes. Add egg mixture and cook, stirring constantly, until eggs begin to set, about 1 minute. Add rice and cook, stirring gently, until heated through, about 2 minutes.

PER SERVING (about 1¼ cups): 244 g, 310 Cal, 7 g Total Fat, 2 g Sat Fat, 0 g Trans Fat, 215 mg Chol, 346 mg Sod, 47 g Total Carb, 4 g Total Sugar, 4 g Fib, 13 g Prot, 48 mg Calc.

8 PointsPlus® value
Per Serving

▲ Healthy Extra **Just before serving, sprinkle the fried rice with a shredded carrot and 3 thinly sliced scallions.**

Bonus Chapter!

THREE-INGREDIENT SIDES

Roasted Sweet Potatoes, Parsnips, and Onion **154**

Buttermilk-Scallion Mashed Potatoes **156**

Cardamom-Coconut Rice **157**

Wild Rice Pilaf with Raisins and Orange **159**

Couscous with Dried Fruit and Pine Nuts **160**

Ginger Beets **161**

Sautéed Sweet Plantains **162**

Maple-Glazed Butternut Squash **164**

Sautéed Escarole with Sun-Dried Tomatoes **165**

Oven-Roasted Kale **167**

Broccolini with Walnuts and Shallots **168**

Roast Tomatoes with Thyme and Olive Oil **169**

7

Roasted Sweet Potatoes, Parsnips, and Onion

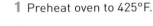

PREP 15 min | **ROAST** 40 min | **SERVES** 4 | **LEVEL** Basic

▲ **3 parsnips, peeled and halved lengthwise**

+

▲ **2 large sweet potatoes, each cut into 8 wedges**

+

▲ **1 large red onion, cut into 8 wedges**

1 Preheat oven to 425°F.

2 Spread parsnips, potatoes, and onion evenly in large roasting pan; lightly spray with olive oil nonstick spray and sprinkle with ¼ teaspoon salt and ¼ teaspoon black pepper. Roast, stirring occasionally, until vegetables are browned and tender, about 40 minutes.

PER SERVING (¾ CUP): 156 g, 158 Cal, 1 g Total Fat, 0 g Sat Fat, 0 g Trans Fat, 0 mg Chol, 195 mg Sod, 37 g Total Carb, 10 g Total Sugar, 7 g Fib, 3 g Prot, 73 mg Calc.

4 PointsPlus® value
Per Serving

▲ Healthy Extra   **Add 1 cup baby cut carrots to the veggie mix before roasting.**

Roasted Sweet Potatoes, Parsnips, and Onion

Buttermilk-Scallion Mashed Potatoes

PREP 10 min | **COOK** 20 min | **SERVES** 4 | **LEVEL** Basic

 1 pound Yukon Gold potatoes

⅓ cup low-fat buttermilk

 4 sliced scallions

1 Peel potatoes and cut into 1½-inch chunks. Put potatoes in medium saucepan and cover with water by 2 inches; bring to boil over high heat. Reduce heat and simmer until tender, 15–18 minutes; drain.

2 Return potatoes to saucepan and add buttermilk and ¼ teaspoon salt; mash with potato masher or large fork until fluffy. Stir in scallions.

PER SERVING (½ cup): **149 g, 106 Cal, 0 g Total Fat, 0 g Sat Fat, 0 g Trans Fat, 1 mg Chol, 176 mg Sod, 22 g Total Carb, 1 g Total Sugar, 2 g Fib, 4 g Prot, 35 mg Calc.**

FYI **If you leave the potatoes unpeeled and then give them just a quick mash with a large fork, you'll have deliciously rustic "smashed" potatoes—and shave about 5 minutes off your prep time.**

Cardamom-Coconut Rice

PREP 5 min | **COOK** 45 min | **SERVES** 6 | **LEVEL** Basic

 ▲ **1 cup brown basmati rice**

+

 1 cup light (reduced-fat) coconut milk

+

 ½ teaspoon ground cardamom

Bring 1 cup water to boil in medium saucepan. Add rice, coconut milk, cardamom, and ¼ teaspoon salt; return to boil. Reduce heat and simmer, covered, until rice is tender, about 40 minutes.

PER SERVING (½ cup): 98 g, 132 Cal, 4 g Total Fat, 0 g Sat Fat, 0 g Trans Fat, 0 mg Chol, 101 mg Sod, 25 g Total Carb, 0 g Total Sugar, 1 g Fib, 3 g Prot, 5 mg Calc.

4 PointsPlus® value
Per Serving

FYI   **For a milder cardamom flavor, use 3 whole green or white cardamom pods instead of ground cardamom; discard the pods just before serving.**

Wild Rice Pilaf with Raisins and Orange

Wild Rice Pilaf with Raisins and Orange

Zest and juice of 1 orange

+

▲ **1 cup brown and wild rice blend**

+

¼ **cup golden raisins**

1 Put ¼ cup of orange juice in medium saucepan, reserving any remaining juice for another use. Add 1½ cups water and ½ teaspoon salt; bring to boil over high heat. Stir in rice. Reduce heat to medium low and simmer, covered, until rice is tender and liquid is absorbed, about 40 minutes.

2 Remove rice from heat; stir in raisins and let sit, covered, 10 minutes. Fluff with fork before serving and sprinkle with orange zest.

PER SERVING (½ cup): 125 g, 156 Cal, 1 g Total Fat, 0 g Sat Fat, 0 g Trans Fat, 0 mg Chol, 201 mg Sod, 33 g Total Carb, 6 g Total Sugar, 3 g Fib, 3 g Prot, 11 mg Calc.

4 PointsPlus® value

Per Serving

▲ Healthy Extra **Stir ½ cup diced onion and ½ cup diced celery into the saucepan when you stir in the rice.**

Couscous with Dried Fruit and Pine Nuts

PREP 5 min	COOK 5 min	SERVES 6	LEVEL Basic

 1 cup whole wheat couscous

+

2 tablespoons diced mixed dried fruit

+

2 tablespoons toasted pine nuts

Bring 1 cup water and ¼ teaspoon salt to boil in medium saucepan; add couscous and dried fruit. Remove saucepan from heat. Let stand, covered, 5 minutes. Fluff gently with fork and sprinkle with pine nuts.

PER SERVING (½ cup): 74 g, 137 Cal, 2 g Total Fat, 0 g Sat Fat, 0 g Trans Fat, 0 mg Chol, 103 mg Sod, 26 g Total Carb, 2 g Total Sugar, 4 g Fib, 5 g Prot, 14 mg Calc.

3 PointsPlus® value
Per Serving

Simple Additions **Stir 1 small cinnamon stick, 1 bay leaf, and 2 whole cloves into the water along with the salt for a deliciously fragrant dish. Use a spoon to scoop out and discard the spices just before you fluff the couscous.**

Ginger Beets

PREP 10 min | **ROAST** 1 hr | **SERVES** 4 | **LEVEL** Intermediate

▲ **1½ pounds small beets**

+

1 teaspoon olive oil

+

2 tablespoons matchstick strips of peeled fresh ginger

1 Preheat oven to 400°F.

2 Trim beets, leaving root and 1 inch of stem intact; scrub skins with brush. Wrap beets securely in foil, place on oven rack and roast until fork-tender, about 1 hour. Unwrap beets and let cool. Slip skins off and cut each beet in half.

3 Heat oil in large nonstick skillet over medium heat. Add ginger and cook, stirring occasionally, until golden, 1–2 minutes. Add beets and ¼ teaspoon salt; heat through. Serve warm or at room temperature.

PER SERVING (¾ cup): 143 g, 86 Cal, 1 g Total Fat, 0 g Sat Fat, 0 g Trans Fat, 0 mg Chol, 278 mg Sod, 17 g Total Carb, 12 g Total Sugar, 5 g Fib, 3 g Prot, 28 mg Calc.

2 PointsPlus® value

Per Serving

▲ Healthy Extra **Make these beets into a colorful, healthful salad by tossing them with 2 grated carrots, 4 cups baby spinach, 1 sliced red bell pepper, and balsamic vinegar to taste.**

Sautéed Sweet Plantains

| **PREP** 5 min | **COOK** 15 min | **SERVES** 4 | **LEVEL** Basic |

1 teaspoon unsalted butter

+

▲ **2 ripe plantains, peeled and cut into ½-inch slices**

+

½ cup pineapple juice

Melt butter in large nonstick skillet over medium heat. Add plantains and cook, turning once, until lightly browned, about 10 minutes. Add pineapple juice and ⅛ teaspoon salt; continue cooking until most liquid has evaporated, about 4 minutes.

PER SERVING (½ cup): 73 g, 134 Cal, 1 g Total Fat, 1 g Sat Fat, 0 g Trans Fat, 3 mg Chol, 77 mg Sod, 33 g Total Carb, 17 g Total Sugar, 2 g Fib, 1 g Prot, 7 mg Calc.

PointsPlus® value

Per Serving

FYI **The peel of a ripe plantain is a deep yellow with black patches or is almost completely black; green, unripe plantains are too dense and starchy to work in this recipe.**

Sautéed Sweet Plantains

Maple-Glazed Butternut Squash

| PREP 5 min | ROAST 25 min | SERVES 4 | LEVEL Basic |

▲ **1 (20-ounce) package cut and peeled butternut squash**

+

2 tablespoons maple syrup

+

2 teaspoons olive oil

1 Preheat oven to 450°F. Spray large baking sheet with nonstick spray.

2 Combine squash, syrup, oil, ¼ teaspoon salt, and ¼ teaspoon black pepper in large bowl; toss to coat. Spread squash mixture in single layer on baking sheet. Roast, stirring every 10 minutes, until squash is tender, about 25 minutes.

PER SERVING (generous ½ cup): 155 g, 111 Cal, 3 g Total Fat, 0 g Sat Fat, 0 g Trans Fat, 0 mg Chol, 152 mg Sod, 23 g Total Carb, 9 g Total Sugar, 3 g Fib, 1 g Prot, 75 mg Calc.

▲ Healthy Extra   **For a deliciously quick soup, blend the cooked squash with 2 cups chicken or vegetable broth and a few pinches of curry powder.**

Sautéed Escarole with Sun-Dried Tomatoes

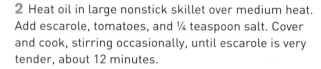

PREP 5 min | **COOK** 15 min | **SERVES** 4 | **LEVEL** Basic

 6 sun-dried tomatoes (not packed in oil)

+

1½ teaspoons olive oil

+

▲ **1 head escarole, sliced**

1 Place tomatoes in small bowl and add ½ cup boiling water; soak until softened, about 10 minutes. Drain and cut into thin strips.

2 Heat oil in large nonstick skillet over medium heat. Add escarole, tomatoes, and ¼ teaspoon salt. Cover and cook, stirring occasionally, until escarole is very tender, about 12 minutes.

PER SERVING (½ cup): 120 g, 53 Cal, 2 g Total Fat, 0 g Sat Fat, 0 g Trans Fat, 0 mg Chol, 179 mg Sod, 7 g Total Carb, 1 g Total Sugar, 5 g Fib, 3 g Prot, 80 mg Calc.

Simple Additions   **For authentic Italian flavor, stir 2 sliced garlic cloves and a few pinches of red pepper flakes into the oil just before you add the escarole.**

Oven-Roasted Kale

Oven-Roasted Kale

PREP 10 min | **ROAST** 10 min | **SERVES** 6 | **LEVEL** Basic

 ▲ **1 (¾-pound) bunch kale, rinsed**

 ¾ teaspoon chili powder

 ½ teaspoon kosher salt

1 Preheat oven to 400°F. Spray 2 large baking sheets with nonstick spray.

2 Trim tough stems from kale and discard; cut large leaves into 2-inch pieces (leave any small leaves whole). Place kale on baking sheets in single layer. Lightly spray with nonstick spray and sprinkle with chili powder and salt. Bake until kale is crispy and edges begin to brown, about 8 minutes.

PER SERVING (1 cup): 30 g, 30 Cal, 1 g Total Fat, 0 g Sat Fat, 0 g Trans Fat, 0 mg Chol, 188 mg Sod, 6 g Total Carb, 0 g Total Sugar, 1 g Fib, 2 g Prot, 77 mg Calc.

PointsPlus® value 1 Per Serving

FYI **This is a delightfully tasty side dish to serve with stews or casseroles. Be sure to pat the kale dry with paper towels after rinsing it.**

Broccolini with Walnuts and Shallots

PREP 10 min | **COOK** 25 min | **SERVES 4** | **LEVEL** Intermediate

▲ **1 pound Broccolini (Asparation), stems trimmed**

+

4 shallots, peeled and halved

+

2 tablespoons chopped toasted walnuts

1 Bring large pot of water to boil. Add Broccolini and cook just until tender, about 4 minutes. Drain, cool under cold running water, and drain again.

2 Spray large nonstick skillet with nonstick spray and set over medium heat. Add shallots and 3 tablespoons water; bring to simmer. Cover and cook until shallots are tender, about 5 minutes. Uncover and cook, stirring occasionally, until water is evaporated and shallots are browned, about 4 minutes longer.

3 Add Broccolini, ¼ teaspoon salt, and ⅛ teaspoon black pepper to skillet; heat through. Sprinkle with walnuts before serving.

PER SERVING (¾ cup): 128 g, 92 Cal, 2 g Total Fat, 0 g Sat Fat, 0 g Trans Fat, 0 mg Chol, 183 mg Sod, 14 g Total Carb, 4 g Total Sugar, 2 g Fib, 5 g Prot, 95 mg Calc.

2 PointsPlus® value
Per Serving

- -

▲ Healthy Extra **Add 1 diced yellow or orange bell pepper to the skillet just after the shallots have become tender.**

Roast Tomatoes with Thyme and Olive Oil

PREP 5 min | **ROAST** 35 min | **SERVES** 6 | **LEVEL** Basic

▲ **6 plum tomatoes, cored and halved lengthwise**

2 teaspoons olive oil

2 teaspoons fresh thyme or ¾ teaspoon dried

1 Preheat oven to 375°F. Spray a shallow baking pan with nonstick spray.

2 Combine tomatoes, oil, thyme, ¼ teaspoon salt, and ⅛ teaspoon pepper in pan; toss to coat. Arrange tomatoes cut side up and roast until flesh is tender and skins wrinkle, 35–40 minutes.

PER SERVING (2 tomato halves): 64 g, 26 Cal, 2 g Total Fat, 0 g Sat Fat, 0 g Trans Fat, 0 mg Chol, 100 mg Sod, 3 g Total Carb, 2 g Total Sugar, 1 g Fib, 1 g Prot, 8 mg Calc.

PointsPlus® value
Per Serving

- -

FYI **The process of roasting tomatoes concentrates and sweetens their flavor, making them an excellent side dish or a fabulous topping for simple grilled or roasted fish or meats. If you have leftovers, refrigerate them in an airtight container up to 3 days.**

SHORT & SWEET

Simple, Scrumptious Desserts

Raspberry-Nectarine Terrine   **172**

Cinnamon-Poached Pears   **174**

Chilled Pear Soup with Almonds   **175**

Cherry Fool   **177**

Pineapple Upside-Down Shortcakes   **178**

Apricot-Oatmeal Crisp   **180**

Cinnamon-Apple Phyllo Purses   **181**

Blueberry-Buttermilk Cobbler   **183**

Spiced Brandy Custards   **184**

Vanilla Bean Panna Cotta   **185**

Chocolate Mousse with Sliced Strawberries   **186**

Chocolate-Ricotta Mousse   **188**

Silky Almond Flans   **189**

Chocolate-Coconut Truffles   **190**

Berries with White Chocolate–Caramel Sauce   **191**

Frozen Coffee-Hazelnut Tarts   **193**

Chocolate–Chocolate Chip Sorbet   **194**

Cantaloupe-Lime Granita   **195**

Lemon-Scented Macaroons   **196**

8

Raspberry-Nectarine Terrine

PREP 15 min | **COOK** 5 min | **SERVES** 8 | **LEVEL** Intermediate

½ **cup sugar**

+

½ **cup lemon juice**

+

2 (¼-ounce) **envelopes unflavored gelatin**

+

▲ **3 small nectarines, yellow or white, halved, pitted, and chopped**

+

▲ **2 (6-ounce) containers raspberries**

1 Heat sugar, 1½ cups water, and pinch salt in medium saucepan over high heat, stirring occasionally, until mixture boils and sugar is dissolved, about 5 minutes. Remove saucepan from heat; stir in lemon juice. Pour 1 cup lemon mixture into small bowl; sprinkle top with gelatin. Let stand until gelatin softens, about 5 minutes.

2 Reheat remaining lemon mixture over medium heat just until hot, about 2 minutes. Remove saucepan from heat. Add gelatin mixture, stirring until dissolved. Pour mixture through sieve set over medium bowl.

3 Combine nectarines and raspberries in 4½ x 8½-inch loaf pan. Pour gelatin mixture over fruit, pressing on fruit so that it is submerged. Cover with plastic wrap and refrigerate until thoroughly chilled and set, at least 4 hours or up to 2 days.

4 To serve, run thin knife around edge of terrine to loosen from pan. Dip bottom of pan into large bowl of hot water for 5 seconds. Unmold terrine onto platter, shaking pan gently to help release the terrine. Cut into 8 (1-inch) slices.

PER SERVING (1 slice): 161 g, 83 Cal, 0 g Total Fat, 0 g Sat Fat, 0 g Trans Fat, 0 mg Chol, 24 mg Sod, 21 g Total Carb, 15 g Total Sugar, 4 g Fib, 3 g Prot, 17 mg Calc.

2 PointsPlus® value ™

Per Serving

Simple Additions **For a colorful and flavorful garnish, sprinkle each serving of the terrine with thinly sliced fresh mint.**

Raspberry-Nectarine Terrine

Cinnamon-Poached Pears

| **PREP** 15 min | **COOK** 45 min | **SERVES** 4 | **LEVEL** Advanced |

 ▲ **4 large ripe pears**

+

 1 large orange

+

 ¾ cup dry red wine

+

 ¾ cup sugar

+

 1 (3-inch) cinnamon stick

1 Peel pears with vegetable peeler. Use melon baller or teaspoon to scoop out core from bottom of each pear. Select large saucepan or small Dutch oven that will hold pears snuggly standing upright.

2 Remove 4 (4-inch) strips of zest from orange with vegetable peeler. Cut orange in half; squeeze ½ cup juice (reserve remaining orange for another use). Combine orange zest and juice, wine, sugar, cinnamon stick, and 4 cups water in saucepan; bring to boil. Boil 10 minutes. Carefully add pears, keeping them upright; add more water if necessary so that pears are almost completely covered. Return liquid to boil. Reduce heat, cover, and simmer until pears are tender when pierced with fork, about 15 minutes.

3 With slotted spoon, transfer pears to large bowl. Return poaching liquid to boil; boil until reduced to 2 cups, 15–20 minutes. Pour syrup through sieve set over small bowl; discard orange zest and cinnamon stick. Cool slightly and serve each pear drizzled with ¼ cup syrup; discard remaining syrup or save for another use.

PER SERVING (1 pear with ¼ cup syrup): 297 g, 210 Cal, 0 g Total Fat, 0 g Sat Fat, 0 g Trans Fat, 0 mg Chol, 3 mg Sod, 53 g Total Carb, 36 g Total Sugar, 7 g Fib, 1 g Prot, 26 mg Calc.

6 PointsPlus® value

Per Serving

FYI **You can also serve these luscious pears chilled.**

Chilled Pear Soup with Almonds

| **PREP** 15 min | **COOK** 10 min | **SERVES** 4 | **LEVEL** Basic |

▲ **3 very ripe pears, peeled, cored, and coarsely chopped**

+

2 cups unsweetened apple juice

+

1 (1-inch) piece fresh ginger, peeled and thinly sliced

+

1 cup pear juice

+

2 tablespoons toasted sliced almonds

1 Bring pears, apple juice, and ginger to boil in large saucepan. Reduce heat, cover, and simmer until pears are very tender, 5–10 minutes (depending on ripeness of fruit). Let cool about 5 minutes.

2 Puree pear mixture in blender, in batches if necessary. Transfer puree to airtight container; stir in pear juice. Let mixture cool completely. Cover and refrigerate until chilled, at least 3 hours or up to 2 days.

3 Divide soup evenly among 4 bowls and sprinkle with sliced almonds.

PER SERVING (1¼ cups soup and ½ tablespoon almonds): 321 g, 182 Cal, 2 g Total Fat, 0 g Sat Fat, 0 g Trans Fat, 0 mg Chol, 11 mg Sod, 42 g Total Carb, 31 g Total Sugar, 5 g Fib, 1 g Prot, 60 mg Calc.

5 PointsPlus® value

Per Serving

▲ Healthy Extra   **Top each serving of soup with ½ cup fresh raspberries.**

Cherry Fool

Cherry Fool

1 cup dried cherries

+

2 tablespoons sugar

+

1 tablespoon cherry-flavored cordial or liqueur

+

½ cup nondairy light whipped topping

+

▲ 1½ cups pitted fresh cherries

1 Bring dried cherries, sugar, and 3 cups water to boil in medium saucepan. Reduce heat, cover, and simmer, stirring occasionally, until cherries are softened, about 5 minutes. Remove saucepan from heat and stir in liqueur. Cool mixture to room temperature.

2 Puree mixture in blender, in batches if necessary. Transfer puree to medium bowl. Gently fold in whipped topping with rubber spatula, folding until blended. Cover and refrigerate until thoroughly chilled, at least 1 hour or overnight. Divide between 6 bowls and serve garnished with fresh cherries.

PER SERVING (½ cup fool and ¼ cup fresh cherries): 183 g, 131 Cal, 1 g Total Fat, 1 g Sat Fat, 0 g Trans Fat, 0 mg Chol, 8 mg Sod, 28 g Total Carb, 20 g Total Sugar, 3 g Fib, 2 g Prot, 21 mg Calc.

3 PointsPlus® value
Per Serving

▲ Healthy Extra **Garnish the fool with 1½ cups fresh blueberries in addition to the fresh cherries.**

Pineapple Upside-Down Shortcakes

PREP 10 min | **BAKE** 10 min | **SERVES 6** | **LEVEL** Basic

¼ cup + 3 teaspoons packed brown sugar

Juice of ½ lemon

½ teaspoon pumpkin-pie spice

▲ **1 (15¼-ounce) can pineapple chunks in juice, drained**

6 refrigerated reduced-fat buttermilk biscuits (from 7½-ounce can)

1 Preheat oven to 425°F. Spray 6-cup muffin pan with nonstick spray.

2 Mix ¼ cup brown sugar, lemon juice, and pie spice in small bowl. Divide sugar mixture evenly among muffin cups; top evenly with pineapple. Add 1 biscuit to each cup, gently pressing it along side of cup to help it adhere. Sprinkle each biscuit with ½ teaspoon of remaining brown sugar.

3 Bake until pineapple mixture is bubbling and biscuits are golden brown, about 12 minutes. Let shortcakes cool in pan 5 minutes. Invert onto large plate and serve warm.

PER SERVING (1 shortcake): 146 g, 259 Cal, 6 g Total Fat, 4 g Sat Fat, 0 g Trans Fat, 0 mg Chol, 594 mg Sod, 49 g Total Carb, 26 g Total Sugar, 2 g Fib, 4 g Prot, 42 mg Calc.

▲ Healthy Extra   **Serve these luscious shortcakes with a dollop of rich Greek yogurt on the side (⅓ cup plain fat-free Greek yogurt has a *PointsPlus* value of *2*).**

Pineapple Upside-Down Shortcakes

Apricot-Oatmeal Crisp

½ cup + 1 tablespoon all-purpose flour

+

6 tablespoons packed brown sugar

+

▲ 2 (15-ounce) cans apricot halves in juice, drained and sliced with ⅓ cup juice reserved

+

2 tablespoons light stick butter, melted

+

1 (34-gram) packet low-sugar maple and brown sugar instant oatmeal mix

1 Preheat oven to 425°F.

2 To make filling, combine 1 tablespoon flour and 3 tablespoons brown sugar in microwavable 8-inch-square baking dish. Add apricots and reserved apricot juice, stirring until blended. Cover dish with wax paper and microwave on High until filling begins to bubble, 4–5 minutes, stirring once halfway through microwaving time.

3 Meanwhile, to make topping, combine butter and remaining 3 tablespoons brown sugar in medium bowl. Add oatmeal mix and remaining ½ cup flour; stir until mixed and crumbly.

4 Remove baking dish from microwave; sprinkle topping evenly over filling. Bake until topping is golden, about 15 minutes. Serve warm.

PER SERVING (½ cup): 192 g, 214 Cal, 3 g Total Fat, 2 g Sat Fat, 0 g Trans Fat, 5 mg Chol, 80 mg Sod, 46 g Total Carb, 31 g Total Sugar, 3 g Fib, 3 g Prot, 50 mg Calc.

▲ Healthy Extra **Stir a peeled cored and diced apple into the baking dish along with the apricots.**

Cinnamon-Apple Phyllo Purses

PREP 20 min | **BAKE** 25 min | **SERVES** 4 | **LEVEL** Intermediate

▲ **2 large Granny Smith apples, peeled and diced**

+

2 tablespoons + 2 teaspoons sugar

+

2 teaspoons all-purpose flour

+

1 teaspoon cinnamon

+

4 (12 x 17-inch) sheets frozen phyllo dough, thawed

1 Preheat oven to 375°F. Spray 4 (8-ounce) custard cups with nonstick spray.

2 To make filling, combine apples, 2 tablespoons sugar, flour, and cinnamon in medium bowl.

3 Lay 1 phyllo sheet on cutting board. (Keep remaining phyllo covered with damp kitchen towel and plastic wrap to prevent it from drying out while you work.) Lightly spray sheet with nonstick spray, then cut into 4 equal rectangles. Stack rectangles. Repeat with remaining dough to make total of 4 stacks.

4 Gently ease 1 stack of phyllo into each custard cup, pressing dough against bottom of each cup. Divide filling evenly among cups. Gather edges of phyllo to partially cover filling; lightly spray tops with nonstick spray. Place cups on rimmed baking sheet; sprinkle tops evenly with remaining 2 teaspoons sugar. Bake until phyllo is golden and filling is bubbling, about 25 minutes. Serve warm.

PER SERVING (1 purse): 136 g, 141 Cal, 2 g Total Fat, 0 g Sat Fat, 0 g Trans Fat, 0 mg Chol, 92 mg Sod, 31 g Total Carb, 17 g Total Sugar, 2 g Fib, 2 g Prot, 14 mg Calc.

4 PointsPlus® value
Per Serving

▲ Healthy Extra **Apples and Cheddar cheese make a delicious combination; serve each phyllo purse with a ¾-ounce slice of fat-free Cheddar cheese (and increase the *PointsPlus* value by *1*).**

Blueberry-Buttermilk Cobbler

Blueberry-Buttermilk Cobbler

PREP 10 min | **BAKE** 30 min | **SERVES** 8 | **LEVEL** Basic

▲ **4 cups fresh blueberries**

+

¼ cup + 2 teaspoons sugar

+

Grated zest of 1 lemon

+

1½ cups low-fat baking mix

+

¾ cup low-fat buttermilk

1 Preheat oven to 400°F. Spray an 8 x 8-inch-square baking dish with nonstick spray.

2 To make filling, combine blueberries, ¼ cup sugar, and lemon zest in large bowl; spoon into baking dish.

3 To make topping, combine baking mix and buttermilk in small bowl, stirring just until blended. Spoon dough evenly over filling; sprinkle top with remaining 2 teaspoons sugar.

4 Bake until topping is golden and filling is bubbling, about 30 minutes. Serve warm.

PER SERVING (⅔ cup): 123 g, 142 Cal, 2 g Total Fat, 0 g Sat Fat, 0 g Trans Fat, 1 mg Chol, 269 mg Sod, 31 g Total Carb, 18 g Total Sugar, 2 g Fib, 3 g Prot, 62 mg Calc.

4 PointsPlus® value

Per Serving

Simple Additions **Sift a teaspoon of powdered sugar on top of the cobbler.**

Spiced Brandy Custards

PREP 15 min | **COOK/BAKE** 35 min | **SERVES** 4 | **LEVEL** Intermediate

1½ cups low-fat (1%) milk

+

▲ 2 large eggs

+

¼ cup brown sugar

+

2 tablespoons brandy

+

⅛ teaspoon allspice

1 Preheat oven to 350°F. Spray 4 (6-ounce) custard cups with nonstick spray.

2 Heat milk in medium saucepan over medium heat just until bubbles form around edges of saucepan.

3 Meanwhile, whisk eggs, brown sugar, brandy, allspice, and pinch salt in medium bowl until blended and no lumps of sugar remain.

4 Remove saucepan from heat; gradually whisk hot milk into egg mixture, whisking until blended. Divide custard evenly among custard cups. Transfer cups to 9-inch-square baking pan. Place pan in oven and add enough hot tap water to pan to come halfway up sides of cups. Bake just until custards are set around edges and still jiggle in center, 30–40 minutes.

5 Carefully remove custard cups from hot water and transfer to rack to cool. Cover with plastic wrap and refrigerate until set, at least 3 hours or overnight.

PER SERVING (1 custard): 136 g, 137 Cal, 3 g Total Fat, 1 g Sat Fat, 0 g Trans Fat, 112 mg Chol, 73 mg Sod, 17 g Total Carb, 17 g Total Sugar, 0 g Fib, 6 g Prot, 119 mg Calc.

4 PointsPlus® value
Per Serving

- -

▲ Healthy Extra **Serve each custard with ½ cup fresh blackberries or raspberries.**

Vanilla Bean Panna Cotta

PREP 10 min | **COOK** 5 min | **SERVES** 4 | **LEVEL** Intermediate

1½ teaspoons unflavored gelatin

+

▲ ¾ cup fat-free half-and-half

+

1 vanilla bean, split

+

1 cup low-fat buttermilk

+

⅓ cup sugar

1 Spray 4 (5-ounce) ramekins or (6-ounce) custard cups with nonstick spray.

2 Sprinkle gelatin over ½ cup half-and-half in small bowl. Let stand until gelatin softens, about 5 minutes.

3 Meanwhile, with edge of small knife, scrape seeds from vanilla bean, reserving both pod and seeds.

4 Combine buttermilk, sugar, remaining ¼ cup half-and-half, and vanilla bean pod and seeds in medium saucepan. Cook over medium heat, whisking occasionally, until sugar is dissolved, about 2 minutes. Remove saucepan from heat; whisk in gelatin mixture, whisking until completely dissolved. Pour panna cotta through sieve set over medium bowl; discard vanilla bean pod. Divide panna cotta evenly among ramekins. Cover and refrigerate until panna cotta is thoroughly chilled and set, at least 4 hours or up to 1 day.

5 To serve, run thin knife around edges of ramekins to loosen panna cotta. Dip bottoms of ramekins, one at a time, into bowl of hot water for about 5 seconds. Unmold by inverting panna cotta onto plates.

PER SERVING (1 panna cotta): 118 g, 99 Cal, 1 g Total Fat, 0 g Sat Fat, 0 g Trans Fat, 2 mg Chol, 104 mg Sod, 19 g Total Carb, 18 g Total Sugar, 0 g Fib, 4 g Prot, 132 mg Calc.

▲ Healthy Extra **Fresh diced mango makes a delicious accompaniment to this luscious custard.**

Chocolate Mousse with Sliced Strawberries

PREP 15 min | **MICROWAVE** 1 min | **SERVES** 6 | **LEVEL** Basic

▲ ⅓ **cup**
fat-free
half-and-half

+

⅔ **cup**
semisweet
chocolate chips

+

▲ ¾ **cup**
fat-free sour
cream

+

1 teaspoon
coffee-flavored
liqueur

+

▲ 1½ **cups**
hulled and sliced
strawberries

1 Microwave half-and-half in medium microwavable bowl on High until very hot, about 30 seconds. Stir in chocolate chips and pinch salt. Let stand about 2 minutes. Whisk until chocolate is melted and mixture is smooth. Let cool to room temperature.

2 With electric mixer on high speed, beat sour cream and liqueur (if using) in medium bowl until light and fluffy, about 2 minutes. With rubber spatula, gently fold half of sour cream mixture into chocolate mixture, folding just until blended. Repeat with remaining sour cream. Cover and refrigerate until thoroughly chilled and set, at least 2 hours or up to 1 day. Scoop mousse into dessert bowls and top with strawberries.

PER SERVING (scant ½ cup mousse and ¼ cup strawberries): 107 g, 172 Cal, 7 g Total Fat, 4 g Sat Fat, 0 g Trans Fat, 3 mg Chol, 57 mg Sod, 25 g Total Carb, 17 g Total Sugar, 2 Fib, 3 g Prot, 64 g Calc.

5 PointsPlus® value
Per Serving

Simple Additions **Sprinkle mint and grated lemon zest over the strawberries.**

Chocolate Mousse with Sliced Strawberries

Chocolate-Ricotta Mousse

¼ cup semisweet chocolate chips

+

▲ 2 cups fat-free ricotta cheese

+

3 tablespoons confectioners' sugar

+

½ teaspoon almond extract

+

½ cup nondairy fat-free whipped topping

1 Put chocolate chips in small microwavable bowl. Microwave on High until melted and very smooth, 30–45 seconds, stirring once halfway through microwaving time.

2 Puree ricotta, confectioners' sugar, and almond extract in food processor or blender. Transfer puree to medium bowl; whisk in melted chocolate. With rubber spatula, gently fold in whipped topping, folding just until blended.

3 Cover mousse and refrigerate until thoroughly chilled, at least 1 hour or up to 1 day. Divide evenly among 6 dessert dishes.

PER SERVING (½ cup): 105 g, 132 Cal, 3 g Total Fat, 2 g Sat Fat, 0 g Trans Fat, 7 mg Chol, 110 mg Sod, 16 g Total Carb, 12 g Total Sugar, 1 g Fib, 11 g Prot, 267 mg Calc.

3 PointsPlus® value · Per Serving

▲ Healthy Extra **Garnish each serving of this chocolaty mousse with fresh or frozen unsweetened raspberries.**

Silky Almond Flans

PREP 20 min | **COOK/BAKE** 55 min | **SERVES** 4 | **LEVEL** Advanced

⅓ **cup + 2 tablespoons sugar**

+

▲ **1 cup fat-free half-and-half**

+

▲ **2 large eggs**

+

¼ **teaspoon almond extract**

1 Preheat oven to 325°F.

2 Combine ⅓ cup sugar and 3 tablespoons water in medium heavy saucepan. Cook over medium heat, stirring occasionally, until sugar is dissolved. Reduce heat and simmer without stirring, brushing down sides of pan with pastry brush dipped in cool water for first few minutes of cooking time. Continue cooking, swirling pan to even out color, until caramel is dark amber, 6–8 minutes. Immediately pour caramel evenly into 4 (6-ounce) ramekins or custard cups; swirl ramekins to coat bottoms and half way up sides. Refrigerate until caramel is set, about 10 minutes.

3 Meanwhile, heat half-and-half in medium saucepan set over medium heat until bubbles form around edges of pan. Whisk eggs, remaining 2 tablespoons sugar, and almond extract in medium bowl. Remove pan from heat; gradually whisk hot half-and-half into egg mixture. Return mixture to pan; cook over medium-low heat, stirring constantly, until slightly thickened, about 3 minutes. Pour custard through sieve set over bowl.

4 Divide custard among ramekins. Transfer ramekins to 9-inch square baking pan. Place pan in oven and add boiling water to pan to come halfway up sides of ramekins. Bake until custards are just set around edges and still jiggle in center, 35–40 minutes. Transfer ramekins to rack and let cool 10 minutes. Cover and refrigerate until chilled and set, at least 4 hours.

5 To serve, run thin knife around flans to loosen them from ramekins. Unmold by inverting flans onto small rimmed plates; spoon any sauce in bottom of ramekins onto flans.

PER SERVING (1 flan): 100 g, 131 Cal, 2 g Total Fat, 1 g Sat Fat, 0 g Trans Fat, 108 mg Chol, 83 mg Sod, 23 g Total Carb, 21 g Total Sugar, 0 g Fib, 5 g Prot, 90 mg Calc.

3 PointsPlus® value

Per Serving

Chocolate-Coconut Truffles

PREP 20 min | **COOK** 5 min | **SERVES** 32 | **LEVEL** Intermediate

**8 ounces
semisweet
chocolate,
chopped**

+

**3 tablespoons
unsalted butter**

+

▲ **⅓ cup
fat-free
half-and-half**

+

**¼ teaspoon
vanilla extract**

+

**6 tablespoons
shredded
sweetened
coconut, finely
chopped**

1 Line 5 x 9-inch loaf pan with plastic wrap; spray wrap with nonstick spray.

2 Combine chocolate and butter in medium saucepan. Cook over low heat, stirring frequently, just until melted and smooth. Remove saucepan from heat; add half-and-half and vanilla, stirring until blended. Transfer mixture to loaf pan and spread evenly. Cover pan with plastic wrap and refrigerate until firm, at least 3 hours or up to 3 days.

3 Spread coconut on plate. Uncover loaf pan and unmold truffle mixture on cutting board; remove plastic wrap. With sharp knife, cut truffle mixture into 8 equal slices. Cut each slice into quarters to make total of 32 squares. Working in batches, lightly coat squares with coconut. Transfer truffles to airtight container, separating layers with sheets of wax paper. Cover and refrigerate up to 1 week.

PER SERVING (1 truffle): 12 g, 52 Cal, 4 g Total Fat, 2 g Sat Fat, 0 g Trans Fat, 3 mg Chol, 5 mg Sod, 5 g Total Carb, 5 g Total Sugar, 0 g Fib, 1 g Prot, 4 mg Calc.

2 PointsPlus® value
Per Serving

Simple Additions   **Kids will love this colorful variation: Toss the coconut with a drop or two of food dye before rolling the truffles in it.**

Berries with
White Chocolate–Caramel Sauce

▲ **3 tablespoons fat-free half-and-half**

+

4½ tablespoons white chocolate chips

+

¼ cup fat-free caramel topping

+

1 tablespoon dark rum

+

▲ **3 (6-ounce) containers fresh berries**

1 To make sauce, combine half-and-half and chocolate chips in small microwavable bowl. Microwave on High just until mixture begins to simmer, 20–30 seconds. Stir until chocolate is melted and completely smooth. Add caramel topping and rum, stirring until blended.

2 Divide berries evenly among 4 dessert dishes; drizzle with warm sauce.

PER SERVING (¾ cup berries and 2 tablespoons sauce): 89 g, 157 Cal, 5 g Total Fat, 2 g Sat Fat, 0 g Trans Fat, 3 mg Chol, 82 mg Sod, 27 g Total Carb, 19 g Total Sugar, 3 g Fib, 2 g Prot, 59 mg Calc.

4 PointsPlus® value

Per Serving

FYI **You may replace the rum with 1 tablespoon strongly brewed coffee if you prefer.**

Frozen Coffee-Hazelnut Tarts

Frozen Coffee-Hazelnut Tarts

PREP 10 min | **COOK** none | **SERVES** 6 | **LEVEL** Basic

1 pint coffee fat-free frozen yogurt

2 tablespoons finely chopped skinned hazelnuts

1 tablespoon hazelnut-flavored liqueur (optional)

1 (4-ounce) package mini–graham cracker pie crusts (6 crusts)

6 teaspoons sugar-free fudge topping

Put frozen yogurt, hazelnuts, and liqueur (if using) in food processor and pulse just until blended, 4–5 times. Spoon ⅓ cup yogurt mixture into each crust; drizzle each with 1 teaspoon fudge topping. Freeze until firm, about 3 hours.

PER SERVING (1 tart with liqueur): 109 g, 242 Cal, 7 g Total Fat, 1 g Sat Fat, 2 g Trans Fat, 3 mg Chol, 151 mg Sod, 38 g Total Carb, 20 g Total Sugar, 1 g Fib, 6 g Prot, 159 mg Calc.

PointsPlus® value
Per Serving

FYI It's important to pulse the frozen yogurt, hazelnuts, and liqueur only a few times in the food processor—if pulsed too much, the yogurt will begin to melt.

Chocolate–Chocolate Chip Sorbet

PREP 20 min | **COOK** 5 min | **SERVES** 10 | **LEVEL** Intermediate

1¼ cups sugar

+

⅔ cup unsweetened Dutch process cocoa

+

⅔ cup + ½ cup mini–chocolate chips

+

2 teaspoons vanilla extract

1 Combine sugar, cocoa, and 2½ cups water in medium heavy saucepan. Bring just to boil over medium-high heat, stirring to dissolve sugar.

2 Remove saucepan from heat; whisk in ⅔ cup chocolate chips, whisking until smooth. Pour mixture through sieve set over medium bowl; stir in vanilla. Let cool to room temperature, about 30 minutes. Cover and refrigerate until thoroughly chilled, at least 3 hours or overnight.

3 Pour mixture into ice-cream maker and freeze according to manufacturer's instructions; add remaining ½ cup chocolate chips in last few minutes of freezing time. Transfer sorbet to freezer container and freeze until firm, at least 2 hours.

PER SERVING (½ cup): **43 g, 164 Cal, 9 g Total Fat, 4 g Sat Fat, 0 g Trans Fat, 0 mg Chol, 2 mg Sod, 31 g Total Carb, 27 g Total Sugar, 2 g Fib, 1 g Prot, 7 mg Calc.**

6 PointsPlus® value

Per Serving

FYI **If you're in a hurry, you can shorten the chilling time by a few hours. Prepare the recipe as directed, but in step 2 set the bowl containing the hot chocolate mixture into a larger bowl half-filled with ice water. Let the mixture stand, stirring occasionally, until thoroughly chilled, about 30 minutes.**

Cantaloupe-Lime Granita

PREP 15 min | **COOK** 5 min | **SERVES** 8 | **LEVEL** Basic

½ **cup sugar**

▲ **6 cups peeled, seeded cantaloupe chunks**

Grated zest and juice of 1 large lime

8 fresh mint sprigs

1 Bring sugar and ½ cup water to boil in small saucepan; boil 3 minutes.

2 Meanwhile, puree cantaloupe in batches in food processor; transfer to large bowl. Stir in sugar syrup and lime zest and juice.

3 Pour mixture into 8-inch-square baking dish. Cover with foil and freeze until partially frozen, about 1½ hours. With fork, scrape chunks into center of pan. Cover and freeze until mixture is completely frozen, scraping with fork every 30 minutes, about 3 hours.

4 To serve, scrape fork across surface of granita, transferring ice shards to 8 dessert dishes. Garnish each dish with 1 mint sprig.

PER SERVING (generous ½ cup): 135 g, 73 Cal, 0 g Total Fat, 0 g Sat Fat, 0 g Trans Fat, 0 mg Chol, 19 mg Sod, 19 g Total Carb, 18 g Total Sugar, 1 g Fib, 1 g Prot, 13 mg Calc.

▲ Healthy Extra **This icy granita is delicious served alongside ricotta cheese (⅓ cup fat-free ricotta per serving will increase the *PointsPlus* value by *2*).**

Lemon-Scented Macaroons

PREP 15 min | **BAKE** 25 min | **SERVES** 16 | **LEVEL** Basic

1 cup slivered almonds

+

⅔ cup sugar

+

▲ 1 large egg white

+

Grated zest of ½ lemon

1 Adjust oven racks to divide oven into thirds; preheat oven to 350°F.

2 Spread almonds on large baking sheet; bake in middle of oven until toasted and fragrant, about 8 minutes. Let cool completely. (Leave oven on.)

3 Transfer almonds to food processor; add sugar and ⅛ teaspoon salt. Pulse until almonds are very finely ground, about 1 minute. Add egg white and lemon zest; pulse 10 times or until dough comes together. Transfer dough to small bowl.

4 Line baking sheet with parchment paper. Drop dough by scant tablespoonfuls onto baking sheet about 2 inches apart, making 16 cookies. Lightly brush cookies with water and press to flatten slightly. Bake in middle of oven until golden, about 15 minutes. Slide parchment paper onto rack and let macaroons cool completely. Peel macaroons off paper.

PER SERVING (1 macaroon): 15 g, 60 Cal, 3 g Total Fat, 0 g Sat Fat, 0 g Trans Fat, 0 mg Chol, 22 mg Sod, 8 g Total Carb, 6 g Total Sugar, 1 g Fib, 2 g Prot, 18 mg Calc.

2 PointsPlus value
Per Serving

▲ Healthy Extra **These light macaroons are a wonderful accompaniment to your next cappuccino break (a cappuccino made with 1 cup fat-free milk and no sugar has a *PointsPlus* value of *2*).**

Chicken, Cheddar, and Apple Panini, page 33

Index

A

Almond extract
Chocolate-Ricotta Mousse, 188
Silky Almond Flans, 189

Almonds
Baby Greens with Gorgonzola and Almonds, 28, *29*
Catfish Amandine, 99
Chilled Pear Soup with Almonds, 175
Lemon-Scented Macaroons, 196

Apple cider, Swordfish Steaks with Caramelized Onions, 96, *97*

Apple juice
Chilled Pear Soup with Almonds, 175
Pork Medallions with Marsala and Mushrooms, 54

Apples
Chicken, Cheddar, and Apple Panini, *32, 33*
Cinnamon-Apple Phyllo Purses, 181
Ham Steaks with Apples and Cranberries, 55

Apricot-Oatmeal Crisp, 180

Arctic char
Honey-Glazed Arctic Char, 93
Souvlaki-Style Fish Kebabs, 143

Artichokes
Artichoke and Garlic Bruschetta, 36
Eggplant–Goat Cheese Rolls, *124, 125*
Pasta with Chicken Sausage and Artichokes, 81

Arugula
Beet Salad with Pecan-Cheese Wedges, 127
Pan-Grilled Tuna and Lemons over Arugula, 94

Asparagus, Chicken with Black Bean Sauce, 72

Avocado, Caribbean Shrimp Tacos, 35

B

Baby Greens with Gorgonzola and Almonds, 28, *29*
Baked Whole Sea Bass with Fennel, 95

Baking mix, Blueberry-Buttermilk Cobbler, *182,* 183

Balsamic dressing
Beet Salad with Pecan-Cheese Wedges, 127
Rosemary-Balsamic Pork Chops, 133

Barbecue sauce, Sweet Chipotle Drumsticks, 77
Barley, Hearty Chicken-Barley Stew, 76
Basil
Eggplant–Goat Cheese Rolls, *124,* 125
Pesto-and-Feta–Stuffed Chicken Breasts, 66, *67*
Spaghetti "Bolognese," *10,* 112, *113*
Two-Tomato French Bread Pizzas, 128, *129*

Basmati rice, Cardamom-Coconut Rice, 157
Beans
Chicken-Chili Cobbler with Polenta, 80
Quick Chicken and Black Bean Burritos, 138, *139*
Red Lentil–and–Black Bean Masala, 122
Rigatoni with Spicy Sausage and Beans, *60,* 61
Roasted Eggplant and Cauliflower Curry, 123
Smoky Greens and Beans with Polenta, 120, *121*

Beef
Beef and Ricotta Lasagna, 48, *49*
Braised Beef Shanks with Wine and Shallots, *46,* 47
Filet Mignon with Garlic Cream Sauce, *3,* 40, *41*
Ginger-Sesame Steak Kebabs, 132
Grilled Flank Steak with Sweet Onions, 43
Hoisin-Marinated London Broil, 42
Napa-Beef Slaw with Ginger Dressing, 26
Spicy Teriyaki Skirt Steak, 44

Beef and Ricotta Lasagna, 48, *49*
Beefy Chili Verde with Poblanos, 45
Beer-Braised Mussels, 147

Beets
Beet Salad with Pecan-Cheese Wedges, 127
Creamy Borscht with Tarragon, 20
Ginger Beets, 161

Beet Salad with Pecan-Cheese Wedges, 127
Berries with White Chocolate–Caramel Sauce, 191

Bell peppers
Chicken-Chili Cobbler with Polenta, 80
Fried Rice with Snow Peas, *150,* 151
Mahimahi with Coconut Curry Sauce, 100
Pan-Fried Shrimp in Red Pepper Sauce, *102,* 103
Simmered Italian-Style Pork Chops, 51
Vegetable-Cheese Frittata, 118

Black beans, Quick Chicken and Black Bean Burritos, 138, *139*

Blending safely, 21

Blueberries

Berries with White Chocolate–Caramel Sauce, 191

Blueberry-Buttermilk Cobbler, *182,* 183

Blue cheese

Penne with Blue Cheese and Squash, 126

Spicy Blue Cheese Turkey Burgers, 85

Braised Beef Shanks with Wine and Shallots, *46,* 47

Braised Chicken Thighs with Tomatoes and Green Olives, 74, *75*

Brandy, Spiced Brandy Custards, 184

Branzini, Baked Whole Sea Bass with Fennel, 95

Bread crumbs, making, 37

Broccoli

Egg and Broccoli Strudel, *116,* 117

Scallop-Broccoli Stir-Fry, 106, *107*

Broccolini with Walnuts and Shallots, *97,* 168

Broth

Mussels in Spicy Garlic Broth, 105

organic low-sodium, 119

Bruschetta, Artichoke and Garlic Bruschetta, 36

Burgers

Spicy Blue Cheese Turkey Burgers, 85

Tuna Teriyaki Burgers, 142

Burritos, Quick Chicken and Black Bean Burritos, 138, *139*

Butterflied Lamb with Couscous Salad, 58, *59*

Buttermilk

Blueberry-Buttermilk Cobbler, *182,* 183

Buttermilk-Scallion Mashed Potatoes, 156

Crispy Cornmeal-Coated Flounder, 98

Crispy Pecan-Crusted Chicken Breasts, 68

Oven-Fried Chicken with Buttermilk Brine, 73

Vanilla Bean Panna Cotta, 185

Butternut squash

Maple-Glazed Butternut Squash, 164

Penne with Blue Cheese and Squash, 126

C

Cabbage

Kielbasa with Cabbage and Caraway, 86

Napa-Beef Slaw with Ginger Dressing, 26

to make quick sauerkraut, 31

Cajun seasoning

Catfish Po'Boys, 144, *145*

Crispy Pecan-Crusted Chicken Breasts, 68

Grilled Flank Steak with Sweet Onions, 43

Calamari, Seafood Salad with Lemon and Orzo, *108,* 109

Cantaloupe-Lime Granita, 195

Capers, Chicken Cutlets with Lemon-Caper Sauce, 137

Caramel topping, Berries with White Chocolate–Caramel Sauce, 191

Caraway, Kielbasa with Cabbage and Caraway, 86

Cardamom, Cardamom-Coconut Rice, 157

Carrots, Napa-Beef Slaw with Ginger Dressing, 26

Catfish

Catfish Amandine, 99

Catfish Po'Boys, 144, *145*

Cauliflower, Roasted Eggplant and Cauliflower Curry, 123

Cayenne pepper, Oven-Fried Chicken with Buttermilk Brine, 73

Cheddar cheese, Chicken, Cheddar, and Apple Panini, *32,* 33, *198*

Cheese

Baby Greens with Gorgonzola and Almonds, 28, *29*

Beef and Ricotta Lasagna, 48, *49*

Beet Salad with Pecan-Cheese Wedges, 127

Chicken, Cheddar, and Apple Panini, *32,* 33, *198*

Chocolate-Ricotta Mousse, 188

Crêpes with Ham, Spinach, and Leek, 56

Egg and Broccoli Strudel, *116,* 117

Eggplant–Goat Cheese Rolls, *124,* 125

Filet Mignon with Garlic Cream Sauce, *3,* 40, *41*

Pan-Toasted Reubens, 30

Penne with Blue Cheese and Squash, 126

Pesto-and-Feta–Stuffed Chicken Breasts, 66, *67*

Quick Chicken and Black Bean Burritos, 138, *139*

Spicy Blue Cheese Turkey Burgers, 85

Spinach and Sun-Dried Tomato Pizza, 149

Tortellini with Chicken and Watercress, *78,* 79

Vegetable-Cheese Frittata, 118

Cherries

Cherry Fool, *8, 176,* 177

Duck with Cherry-Tarragon Glaze, 87

Loin of Pork Stuffed with Cherries, *52,* 53

Chicken

Braised Chicken Thighs with Tomatoes and Green Olives, 74, *75*

Chicken, Cheddar, and Apple Panini, *32,* 33, *198*

Chicken Breasts with Garlic and Orange, 65

Chicken-Chili Cobbler with Polenta, 80

Chicken Cutlets with Lemon-Caper Sauce, 137

Chicken Kebabs with Lime and Pineapple, *14, 70,* 71

Chicken Roulades with Prosciutto and Sage, 69

Chicken with Black Bean Sauce, 72

Crispy Pecan-Crusted Chicken Breasts, 68

Curried Chicken Salad, *24,* 25

Hearty Chicken-Barley Stew, 76

Oven-Fried Chicken with Buttermilk Brine, 73

Pasta with Chicken Sausage and Artichokes, 81

Quick Chicken and Black Bean Burritos, 138, *139*

Smoked-Chicken and Mango Wraps, 34

Sweet-and-Spicy Roast Chicken, 64

Sweet Chipotle Drumsticks, 77

Tortellini with Chicken and Watercress, *78,* 79

Chicken, Cheddar, and Apple Panini, 32, 33, *198*
Chicken Breasts with Garlic and Orange, 65
Chicken-Chili Cobbler with Polenta, 80
Chicken Cutlets with Lemon-Caper Sauce, 137
Chicken Kebabs with Lime and Pineapple, *14,
70*, 71
Chicken Roulades with Prosciutto and Sage, 69
Chicken with Black Bean Sauce, 72
Chickpeas, Roasted Eggplant and Cauliflower
Curry, 123
Chile peppers
Beefy Chili Verde with Poblanos, 45
Chicken Kebabs with Lime and Pineapple, 71
safety, 45
Spicy Teriyaki Skirt Steak, 44
Chili
Beefy Chili Verde with Poblanos, 45
Chicken-Chili Cobbler with Polenta, 80
Chili powder
Lime-and-Chili–Grilled Shrimp, 148
Oven-Roasted Kale, *14, 166*, 167
Chilled Pear Soup with Almonds, 175
Chinese Egg-Flower Soup, 18, *19*
Chipotle peppers
Smoky Greens and Beans with Polenta, 120, *121*
Sweet-and-Spicy Roast Chicken, 64
Sweet Chipotle Drumsticks, 77
Chocolate
Berries with White Chocolate–Caramel Sauce, 191
Chocolate–Chocolate Chip Sorbet, 194
Chocolate-Coconut Truffles, 190
Chocolate Mousse with Sliced Strawberries,
186, *187*
Chocolate-Ricotta Mousse, 188
Chocolate–Chocolate Chip Sorbet, 194
Chocolate-Coconut Truffles, 190
Chocolate Mousse with Sliced Strawberries, 186, *187*
Chocolate-Ricotta Mousse, 188
Cilantro
Grilled Flank Steak with Sweet Onions, 43
Red Lentil–and–Black Bean Masala, 122
Roasted Eggplant and Cauliflower Curry, 123
Roast Salmon with Cilantro and Lime, 92
Sweet Chipotle Drumsticks, 77
Tex-Mex Salmon Salad, 30
Tuna Teriyaki Burgers, 142
Cinnamon-Apple Phyllo Purses, 181
Cinnamon-Poached Pears, 174
Clams, Stuffed Clams with Shallots and Lemon, 37
Cobbler
Blueberry-Buttermilk Cobbler, *182*, 183
Chicken-Chili Cobbler with Polenta, 80
Cocoa, Chocolate–Chocolate Chip Sorbet, 194
Coconut
Cardamom-Coconut Rice, 157

Chocolate-Coconut Truffles, 190
Coconut Turkey Fingers with Peach Sauce, 82, *83*
Mahimahi with Coconut Curry Sauce, 100
Cod, Souvlaki-Style Fish Kebabs, 143
Cookies, Lemon-Scented Macaroons, 196
Coriander seeds, Coriander-Mint Lamb Chops, 57
Cornmeal, Crispy Cornmeal-Coated Flounder, 98
Couscous
Butterflied Lamb with Couscous Salad, 58, *59*
Couscous with Dried Fruit and Pine Nuts, 160
Cranberries, Ham Steaks with Apples and
Cranberries, 55
Cream cheese, Crêpes with Ham, Spinach, and Leek,
56
Creamy Borscht with Tarragon, 20
Cremini mushrooms, Grilled Pork and Veggie
Skewers, *134*, 135
Crêpes with Ham, Spinach, and Leek, 56
Crispy Cornmeal-Coated Flounder, 98
Crispy Pecan-Crusted Chicken Breasts, 68
Cucumbers, Grilled Turkey with Plums and Greens,
140, 141
Cumin
Lemon-Cumin Halibut Steaks, 146
Lime-and-Chili–Grilled Shrimp, 148
Curried Chicken Salad, *24*, 25
Curry
Coconut Turkey Fingers with Peach Sauce, 82, *83*
Curried Chicken Salad, *24*, 25
Mahimahi with Coconut Curry Sauce, 100
Red Lentil–and–Black Bean Masala, 122
Roasted Eggplant and Cauliflower Curry, 123
Custard
Silky Almond Flans, 189
Spiced Brandy Custards, 184
Vanilla Bean Panna Cotta, 185

D
Desserts
Apricot-Oatmeal Crisp, 180
Berries with White Chocolate–Caramel Sauce, 191
Blueberry-Buttermilk Cobbler, *182, 183*
Cantaloupe-Lime Granita, 195
Cherry Fool, *8, 176, 177*
Chilled Pear Soup with Almonds, 175
Chocolate–Chocolate Chip Sorbet, 194
Chocolate-Coconut Truffles, 190
Chocolate Mousse with Sliced Strawberries,
186, *187*
Chocolate-Ricotta Mousse, 188
Cinnamon-Apple Phyllo Purses, 181
Cinnamon-Poached Pears, 174
Frozen Coffee-Hazelnut Tarts, *192, 193*
Lemon-Scented Macaroons, 196
Pineapple Upside-Down Shortcakes, 178, *179*

Raspberry-Nectarine Terrine, 172, *173*
Silky Almond Flans, 189
Spiced Brandy Custards, 184
Vanilla Bean Panna Cotta, 185
Dill, Vegetarian Avgolemono with Dill, 119
Dried fruit
Cherry Fool, *8, 176,* 177
Couscous with Dried Fruit and Pine Nuts, 160
Duck with Cherry-Tarragon Glaze, 87

E
Egg and Broccoli Strudel, *116,* 117
Eggplant
Eggplant–Goat Cheese Rolls, *124,* 125
Roasted Eggplant and Cauliflower Curry, 123
Eggs
Chinese Egg-Flower Soup, 18, *19*
Egg and Broccoli Strudel, *116,* 117
Fried Rice with Snow Peas, *150,* 151
Vegetable-Cheese Frittata, 118
Vegetarian Avgolemono with Dill, 119
Escarole, Sautéed Escarole with Sun-Dried
Tomatoes, 165

F
Fennel
Baked Whole Sea Bass with Fennel, 95
Mediterranean Lamb Chops, 136
Feta cheese, Pesto-and-Feta–Stuffed Chicken
Breasts, 66, *67*
Filet Mignon with Garlic Cream Sauce, *3,* 40, *41*
Fish and seafood
Baked Whole Sea Bass with Fennel, 95
Beer-Braised Mussels, 147
Caribbean Shrimp Tacos, 35
Catfish Amandine, 99
Catfish Po'Boys, 144, *145*
Crispy Cornmeal-Coated Flounder, 98
Honey-Glazed Arctic Char, 93
Lemon-Cumin Halibut Steaks, 146
Lime-and-Chili–Grilled Shrimp, 148
Lobster Ravioli with Plum Tomato Sauce, 104
Mahimahi with Coconut Curry Sauce, 100
Mussels in Spicy Garlic Broth, 105
Niçoise-Style Tuna and Rice Salad, 27
Pan-Fried Shrimp in Red Pepper Sauce, *102,* 103
Pan-Grilled Tuna and Lemons Over Arugula, 94
Pea Soup with Smoked Salmon, 21
Poached Salmon with Wasabi Mayonnaise, *90,* 91
removing bones from, 91
Roast Salmon with Cilantro and Lime, 92
Scallop-Broccoli Stir-Fry, 106, *107*
Seafood Salad with Lemon And Orzo, *108,* 109
Souvlaki-Style Fish Kebabs, 143
Striped Bass with Warm Sherry Vinaigrette, 101
Swordfish Steaks with Caramelized Onions, 96, *97*

Tex-Mex Salmon Salad, 30
Tuna Teriyaki Burgers, 142
Flans, Silky Almond Flans, 189
Flounder, Crispy Cornmeal-Coated Flounder, 98
Fried Rice with Snow Peas, *150,* 151
Frozen desserts
Cantaloupe-Lime Granita, 195
Chocolate–Chocolate Chip Sorbet, 194
Frozen Coffee-Hazelnut Tarts, *192, 193*
Fruit
Berries with White Chocolate–Caramel Sauce, 191
Blueberry-Buttermilk Cobbler, *182,* 183
Cherry Fool, *8, 176,* 177
Chicken, Cheddar, and Apple Panini, *32, 33, 198*
Chicken Breasts with Garlic and Orange, 65
Chicken Kebabs with Lime and Pineapple, *14, 70,* 71
Chocolate Mousse with Sliced Strawberries, 186, *187*
Cinnamon-Poached Pears, 174
Couscous with Dried Fruit and Pine Nuts, 160
Grilled Pork Tenderloin with Orange and
Rosemary, 50
Grilled Turkey with Plums and Greens, *140,* 141
Loin of Pork Stuffed with Cherries, *52,* 53
Raspberry-Nectarine Terrine, 172, *173*
Fudge topping, Frozen Coffee-Hazelnut Tarts, *192,* 193

G
Garam masala
recipe for, 122
Red Lentil–and–Black Bean Masala, 122
Garlic
Artichoke and Garlic Bruschetta, 36
Chicken Breasts with Garlic and Orange, 65
Filet Mignon with Garlic Cream Sauce, *3,* 40, *41*
Mussels in Spicy Garlic Broth, 105
Garlic-and-herb cheese, Beet Salad with Pecan-
Cheese Wedges, 127
Ginger
Chicken with Black Bean Sauce, 72
Ginger Beets, 161
Ginger-Sesame Steak Kebabs, 132
grating, 132
Hoisin-Marinated London Broil, 42
Honey-Glazed Arctic Char, 93
Napa-Beef Slaw with Ginger Dressing, 26
Tuna Teriyaki Burgers, 142
Goat cheese
Eggplant–Goat Cheese Rolls, *124,* 125
Spinach and Sun-Dried Tomato Pizza, 149
Gorgonzola cheese, Baby Greens with Gorgonzola and
Almonds, 28, *29*
Graham cracker pie crusts, Frozen Coffee-Hazelnut
Tarts, *192, 193*
Granita, Cantaloupe-Lime Granita, 195
Granny Smith apples
Chicken, Cheddar, and Apple Panini, *32, 33, 198*
Cinnamon-Apple Phyllo Purses, 181

Grilled Flank Steak with Sweet Onions, 43
Grilled Pork and Veggie Skewers, *134, 135*
Grilled Pork Tenderloin with Orange and Rosemary, 50

H

Halibut, Lemon-Cumin Halibut Steaks, 146
Ham Steaks with Apples and Cranberries, 55
Hazelnuts, Frozen Coffee-Hazelnut Tarts, *192, 193*
Hearty Chicken-Barley Stew, 76
Hoisin sauce
    Hoisin-Marinated London Broil, 42
    Tofu and Shiitake Stir-Fry, 115
Honey-Glazed Arctic Char, 93
Horseradish, Poached Salmon with Wasabi
    Mayonnaise, *90, 91*
Hot liquids, blending safely, 21
Hot pepper sauce, Spicy Blue Cheese Turkey Burgers,
    85
Hot sauce, mango, 35

I

Italian cheese blend, Spinach and Sun-Dried Tomato
    Pizza, 149
Italian seasoning, Grilled Pork and Veggie Skewers,
    134, 135

J

Jalapeño pepper, Chicken Kebabs with Lime and
    Pineapple, *70, 71*
Jarlsberg cheese, Egg and Broccoli Strudel, *116, 117*

K

Kale
    Oven-Roasted Kale, *14, 166, 167*
    preparation of, 167
    Rigatoni with Spicy Sausage and Beans, *60, 61*
    Smoky Greens and Beans with Polenta, 120, *121*
Kebabs
    Chicken Kebabs with Lime and Pineapple, *14, 70,*
    71
    Ginger-Sesame Steak Kebabs, 132
    Grilled Pork and Veggie Skewers, *134, 135*
    Souvlaki-Style Fish Kebabs, 143
Kidney beans, Smoky Greens and Beans with Polenta,
    120, *121*
Kielbasa with Cabbage and Caraway, 86

L

Lamb
    Butterflied Lamb with Couscous Salad, 58, *59*
    Coriander-Mint Lamb Chops, 57
    Mediterranean Lamb Chops, 136
Leeks
    Crêpes with Ham, Spinach, and Leek, 56
    Hearty Chicken-Barley Stew, 76
Lemon-Cumin Halibut Steaks, 146

Lemons
    Chicken Cutlets with Lemon-Caper Sauce, 137
    Honey-Glazed Arctic Char, 93
    Lemon-Cumin Halibut Steaks, 146
    Lemon-Scented Macaroons, 196
    Pan-Grilled Tuna and Lemons over Arugula, 94
    Seafood Salad with Lemon and Orzo, *108, 109*
    Souvlaki-Style Fish Kebabs, 143
    Stuffed Clams with Shallots and Lemon, 37
    Vegetarian Avgolemono with Dill, 119
Lemon-Scented Macaroons, 196
Lentils, Red Lentil–and–Black Bean Masala, 122
Limes
    Cantaloupe-Lime Granita, 195
    Chicken Kebabs with Lime and Pineapple, *14, 70, 71*
    Lime-and-Chili–Grilled Shrimp, 148
    Roast Salmon with Cilantro and Lime, 92
Lobster Ravioli with Plum Tomato Sauce, 104
Loin of Pork Stuffed with Cherries, *52, 53*

M

Mahimahi with Coconut Curry Sauce, 100
Mango, Smoked-Chicken and Mango Wraps, 34
Mango hot sauce, 35
Maple syrup, Maple-Glazed Butternut Squash, 164
Marinara sauce
    Beef and Ricotta Lasagna, 48, *49*
    Pan-Fried Shrimp in Red Pepper Sauce, *102, 103*
    Pasta with Chicken Sausage and Artichokes, 81
    Simmered Italian-Style Pork Chops, 51
    Spaghetti "Bolognese," *10*, 112, *113*
Marsala wine, Pork Medallions with Marsala and
    Mushrooms, 54
Measurement equivalents, 208
Measuring, 6–7
Meat, lean, 6
Meatless entrées
    Beet Salad with Pecan-Cheese Wedges, 127
    Egg and Broccoli Strudel, *116, 117*
    Eggplant–Goat Cheese Rolls, *124, 125*
    Fried Rice with Snow Peas, *150, 151*
    Penne with Blue Cheese and Squash, 126
    Red Lentil–and–Black Bean Masala, 122
    Roasted Eggplant and Cauliflower Curry, 123
    Smoky Greens and Beans with Polenta, 120, *121*
    Spaghetti "Bolognese," *10*, 112, *113*
    Spinach and Sun-Dried Tomato Pizza, 149
    Stuffed Portobello Mushrooms, 114
    Tofu and Shiitake Stir-Fry, 115
    Two-Tomato French Bread Pizzas, 128, *129*
    Vegetable-Cheese Frittata, 118
    Vegetarian Avgolemono with Dill, 119
Mediterranean Lamb Chops, 136
Melons, Cantaloupe-Lime Granita, 195
Mexican cheese blend, Quick Chicken and Black Bean
    Burritos, 138, *139*

Mint
    Cantaloupe-Lime Granita, 195
    Coriander-Mint Lamb Chops, 57
Miso, Soba-Noodle Soup with Miso, 22
Mousse
    Chocolate Mousse with Sliced Strawberries, 186, *187*
    Chocolate-Ricotta Mousse, 188
Mozzarella cheese
    Beef and Ricotta Lasagna, 48, *49*
    Vegetable-Cheese Frittata, 118
Mushrooms
    Grilled Pork and Veggie Skewers, *134,* 135
    Hearty Chicken-Barley Stew, 76
    Pork Medallions with Marsala and Mushrooms, 54
    Soba-Noodle Soup with Miso, 22
    Spaghetti "Bolognese," *10,* 112, *113*
    Stuffed Portobello Mushrooms, 114
    Tofu and Shiitake Stir-Fry, 115
Mussels
    Beer-Braised Mussels, 147
    cleaning, 147
    Mussels in Spicy Garlic Broth, 105
    Seafood Salad with Lemon and Orzo, *108,* 109
Mustard
    Chicken, Cheddar, and Apple Panini, *32,* 33, *198*
    Pan-Glazed Turkey Tenderloin, 84
    Tuna Teriyaki Burgers, 142

N

Napa-Beef Slaw with Ginger Dressing, 26
Nectarines, Raspberry-Nectarine Terrine, 172, *173*
Niçoise-Style Tuna and Rice Salad, 27
Nondairy topping
    Cherry Fool, *8, 176,* 177
    Chocolate-Ricotta Mousse, 188
Nuts
    Baby Greens with Gorgonzola and Almonds, 28, *29*
    Beet Salad with Pecan-Cheese Wedges, 127
    Broccolini with Walnuts and Shallots, *97,* 168
    Catfish Amandine, 99
    Chilled Pear Soup with Almonds, 175
    Couscous with Dried Fruit and Pine Nuts, 160
    Crispy Pecan-Crusted Chicken Breasts, 68
    Frozen Coffee-Hazelnut Tarts, *192, 193*
    Lemon-Scented Macaroons, 196

O

Oatmeal, Apricot-Oatmeal Crisp, 180
Olives
    Braised Chicken Thighs with Tomatoes and Green Olives, 74, *75*
    Niçoise-Style Tuna and Rice Salad, 27
Onions
    Grilled Flank Steak with Sweet Onions, 43
    Roasted Sweet Potatoes, Parsnips, and Onion, 154, *155*

    Swordfish Steaks with Caramelized Onions, 96, *97*
Oranges
    Chicken Breasts with Garlic and Orange, 65
    Cinnamon-Poached Pears, 174
    Grilled Pork Tenderloin with Orange and Rosemary, 50
    Spicy Teriyaki Skirt Steak, 44
    Wild Rice Pilaf with Raisins and Orange, *90, 158,* 159
Oregano, Souvlaki-Style Fish Kebabs, 143
Orzo
    Seafood Salad with Lemon and Orzo, *108,* 109
    Vegetarian Avgolemono with Dill, 119
Oven-Fried Chicken with Buttermilk Brine, 73
Oven-Roasted Kale, *14, 166,* 167

P

Pan-Fried Shrimp in Red Pepper Sauce, *102,* 103
Pan-Glazed Turkey Tenderloin, 84
Pan-Grilled Tuna and Lemons over Arugula, 94
Paninis, Chicken, Cheddar, and Apple Panini, *32,* 33, *198*
Panko
    Coconut Turkey Fingers with Peach Sauce, 82, *83*
    Oven-Fried Chicken with Buttermilk Brine, 73
Panna cotta, Vanilla Bean Panna Cotta, 185
Pan-Toasted Reubens, 31
Papaya, Caribbean Shrimp Tacos, 35
Parmesan cheese, Tortellini with Chicken and Watercress, *78,* 79
Parsnips
    Parsnip Soup with Smoked Paprika, 23
    Roasted Sweet Potatoes, Parsnips, and Onion, 154, *155*
Pasta
    Beef and Ricotta Lasagna, 48, *49*
    Butterflied Lamb with Couscous Salad, 58, *59*
    Lobster Ravioli with Plum Tomato Sauce, 104
    Pasta with Chicken Sausage and Artichokes, 81
    Penne with Blue Cheese and Squash, 126
    Rigatoni with Spicy Sausage and Beans, *60,* 61
    Seafood Salad with Lemon and Orzo, *108,* 109
    Soba-Noodle Soup with Miso, 22
    Spaghetti "Bolognese," *10,* 112, *113*
    Tortellini with Chicken and Watercress, *78,* 79
    Vegetarian Avgolemono with Dill, 119
Pastrami, turkey, Pan-Toasted Reubens, 31
Peach, Coconut Turkey Fingers with Peach Sauce, 82, *83*
Pears
    Chilled Pear Soup with Almonds, 175
    Cinnamon-Poached Pears, 174
Peas
    Chinese Egg-Flower Soup, 18, *19*
    Fried Rice with Snow Peas, *150,* 151
    Pea Soup with Smoked Salmon, 21
Pecans
    Beet Salad with Pecan-Cheese Wedges, 127
    Crispy Pecan-Crusted Chicken Breasts, 68

Penne with Blue Cheese and Squash, 126
Peppers. *See also* **bell peppers** *and* **chile peppers**
    Beefy Chili Verde with Poblanos, 45
    Chicken-Chili Cobbler with Polenta, 80
    Chicken Kebabs with Lime and Pineapple, *70*, 71
    Fried Rice with Snow Peas, *150*, 151
    Pan-Fried Shrimp in Red Pepper Sauce, *102*, 103
    safety, 45
    Spicy Teriyaki Skirt Steak, 44
    Sweet Chipotle Drumsticks, 77
    Vegetable-Cheese Frittata, 118
Pesto
    Pesto-and-Feta–Stuffed Chicken Breasts, 66, *67*
    Two-Tomato French Bread Pizzas, 128, *129*
Phyllo dough
    Cinnamon-Apple Phyllo Purses, 181
    Egg and Broccoli Strudel, *116*, 117
Pilaf, Wild Rice Pilaf with Raisins and Orange, *90*,
    158, 159
Pineapple
    Chicken Kebabs with Lime and Pineapple, *14, 70*, 71
    Pineapple Upside-Down Shortcakes, 178, *179*
Pineapple juice, Sautéed Sweet Plantains, 162, *163*
Pine nuts, Couscous with Dried Fruit and Pine Nuts, 160
Pizza
    Spinach and Sun-Dried Tomato Pizza, 149
    Two-Tomato French Bread Pizzas, 128, *129*
Plantains
    peeling, 162
    Sautéed Sweet Plantains, 162, *163*
Plums, Grilled Turkey with Plums and Greens,
    140, 141
Poached Salmon with Wasabi Mayonnaise, *90*, 91
Poblano peppers, Beefy Chili Verde With Poblanos, 45
Po' Boys, Catfish Po' Boys, 144, *145*
Polenta
    Chicken-Chili Cobbler With Polenta, 80
    prepared, 80
    Smoky Greens and Beans with Polenta, 120, *121*
Pork
    Chicken Roulades with Prosciutto and Sage, 69
    Crêpes with Ham, Spinach, and Leek, 56
    Grilled Pork and Veggie Skewers, *134*, 135
    Grilled Pork Tenderloin with Orange and
        Rosemary, 50
    Ham Steaks with Apples and Cranberries, 55
    Loin of Pork Stuffed with Cherries, *52*, 53
    Pork Medallions with Marsala and Mushrooms, 54
    Rigatoni with Spicy Sausage and Beans, *60*, 61
    Rosemary-Balsamic Pork Chops, 133
    Simmered Italian-Style Pork Chops, 51
Portobello mushrooms, Stuffed Portobello
    Mushrooms, 114
Potatoes
    Buttermilk-Scallion Mashed Potatoes, 156
    Roasted Sweet Potatoes, Parsnips, and Onion,
        154, *155*

Preserves
    Coconut Turkey Fingers with Peach Sauce, 82, *83*
    Duck with Cherry-Tarragon Glaze, 87
    Loin of Pork Stuffed with Cherries, *52*, 53
    Pan-Glazed Turkey Tenderloin, 84
Produce, 6
Prosciutto, Chicken Roulades with Prosciutto and
    Sage, *69*

Q
Quick Chicken and Black Bean Burritos, 138, *139*

R
Raisins, Wild Rice Pilaf with Raisins and Orange, *90*,
    158, 159
Raspberry-Nectarine Terrine, 172, *173*
Raspberry vinaigrette, Grilled Turkey with Plums and
    Greens, *140*, 141
Ravioli, Lobster Ravioli with Plum Tomato Sauce, 104
Red Lentil–and–Black Bean Masala, 122
Rice
    Cardamom-Coconut Rice, 157
    Fried Rice with Snow Peas, *150*, 151
    Niçoise-Style Tuna and Rice Salad, 27
    Wild Rice Pilaf with Raisins and Orange, *90*,
        158, 159
Ricotta cheese
    Beef and Ricotta Lasagna, 48, *49*
    Chocolate-Ricotta Mousse, 188
    Two-Tomato French Bread Pizzas, 128, *129*
Rigatoni with Spicy Sausage and Beans, *60*, 61
Roasted Eggplant and Cauliflower Curry, 123
Roasted Sweet Potatoes, Parsnips, and Onion,
    154, *155*
Roast Salmon with Cilantro and Lime, 92
Roast Tomatoes with Thyme and Olive Oil, *3*,
    41, 169
Rosemary
    Grilled Pork Tenderloin with Orange and
        Rosemary, 50
    Rosemary-Balsamic Pork Chops, 133
Rye bread, Pan-Toasted Reubens, 31

S
Sage, Chicken Roulades with Prosciutto and Sage, 69
Salads
    Baby Greens with Gorgonzola and Almonds,
        28, *29*
    Beet Salad with Pecan-Cheese Wedges, 127
    Butterflied Lamb with Couscous Salad, 58, *59*
    Curried Chicken Salad, *24*, 25
    Grilled Turkey with Plums and Greens, *140*, 141
    Napa-Beef Slaw with Ginger Dressing, 26
    Niçoise-Style Tuna and Rice Salad, 27
    Seafood Salad with Lemon and Orzo, *108*, 109
    Tex-Mex Salmon Salad, 30

Salmon
    Pea Soup with Smoked Salmon, 21
    Poached Salmon with Wasabi Mayonnaise, *90, 91*
    removing bones, 91
    Roast Salmon with Cilantro and Lime, 92
    Tex-Mex Salmon Salad, 30

Salsa
    Beefy Chili Verde with Poblanos, 45
    Corn salsa, 43
    Quick Chicken and Black Bean Burritos, 138, *139*
    Tex-Mex Salmon Salad, 30

Sandwiches
    Catfish Po' Boys, 144, *145*
    Chicken, Cheddar, and Apple Panini, *32, 33, 198*
    Pan-Toasted Reubens, 31
    Smoked-Chicken and Mango Wraps, 34

Sauerkraut
    Kielbasa with Cabbage and Caraway, 86
    Pan-Toasted Reubens, 31
    substitutions, 31

Sausage
    Kielbasa with Cabbage and Caraway, 86
    Pasta with Chicken Sausage and Artichokes, 81
    Rigatoni with Spicy Sausage And Beans, *60, 61*
    Stuffed Portobello Mushrooms, 114

Sautéed Escarole with Sun-Dried Tomatoes, 165
Sautéed Sweet Plantains, 162, *163*
Scallions, Buttermilk-Scallion Mashed Potatoes, 156
Scallops
    Scallop-Broccoli Stir-Fry, 106, *107*
    Seafood Salad with Lemon and Orzo, *108,* 109
Sea bass, Baked Whole Sea Bass with Fennel, 95
Seafood, about, 6. *See also* Fish and seafood
Seeds, about crushing, 57
Sesame oil
    Chicken with Black Bean Sauce, 72
    Ginger-Sesame Steak Kebabs, 132
    Tofu and Shiitake Stir-Fry, 115

Shallots
    Braised Beef Shanks with Wine and Shallots, 46, 47
    Broccolini with Walnuts and Shallots, *97,* 168
    Stuffed Clams with Shallots and Lemon, 37
Sherry vinegar, Striped Bass with Warm Sherry Vinaigrette, 101
Shiitake mushrooms, Tofu and Shiitake Stir-Fry, 115
Shopping for ingredients, 6
Shrimp
    Caribbean Shrimp Tacos, 35
    Lime-and-Chili–Grilled Shrimp, 148
    Pan-Fried Shrimp in Red Pepper Sauce, *102,* 103
    Seafood Salad with Lemon and Orzo, *108,* 109
Side dishes
    Broccolini with Walnuts and Shallots, 168
    Buttermilk-Scallion Mashed Potatoes, 156
    Cardamom-Coconut Rice, 157
    Couscous with Dried Fruit and Pine Nuts, 160
    Ginger Beets, 161
    Maple-Glazed Butternut Squash, 164
    Oven-Roasted Kale, *14, 70, 166, 167*
    Roasted Sweet Potatoes, Parsnips, and Onion, 154, *155*
    Roast Tomatoes with Thyme and Olive Oil, *3, 41,* 169
    Sautéed Escarole with Sun-Dried Tomatoes, 165
    Sautéed Sweet Plantains, 162, *163*
    Wild Rice Pilaf with Raisins and Orange, *90, 158,* 159

Silky Almond Flans, 189
Simmered Italian-Style Pork Chops, 51
Simmer sauce, about, 123
Skewers, soaking, 135
Skillets, ovenproof, 68
Smoked-Chicken and Mango Wraps, 34
Smoky Greens and Beans with Polenta, 120, *121*
Snow Peas, Fried Rice with Snow Peas, *150,* 151
Soba-Noodle Soup with Miso, 22
Sorbet, Chocolate–Chocolate Chip Sorbet, 194
Soups
    Chilled Pear Soup with Almonds, 175
    Chinese Egg-Flower Soup, 18, *19*
    Creamy Borscht with Tarragon, 20
    Parsnip Soup with Smoked Paprika, 22
    Pea Soup with Smoked Salmon, 21
    Soba-Noodle Soup with Miso, 22
    Vegetarian Avgolemono with Dill, 119
Souvlaki-Style Fish Kebabs, 143
Soy crumbles, Spaghetti "Bolognese," *10,* 112, *113*
Soy sauce
    Fried Rice with Snow Peas, *150,* 151
    Honey-Glazed Arctic Char, 93
Spaghetti "Bolognese," *10,* 112, *113*
Spiced Brandy Custards, 184
Spices, toasting, 25
Spicy Blue Cheese Turkey Burgers, 85
Spicy Teriyaki Skirt Steak, 44
Spinach
    Crêpes with Ham, Spinach, and Leek, 56
    preparing, 149
    Spinach and Sun-Dried Tomato Pizza, 149
Squash
    Maple-Glazed Butternut Squash, 164
    Penne with Blue Cheese and Squash, 126
Stews, Hearty Chicken-Barley Stew, 76
Stir-fry
    Scallop-Broccoli Stir-Fry, 106, *107*
    Tofu and Shiitake Stir-Fry, 115
Strawberries
    Berries with White Chocolate–Caramel Sauce, 191
    Chocolate Mousse with Sliced Strawberries, 186, *187*
Striped Bass with Warm Sherry Vinaigrette, 101
Strudel, Egg and Broccoli Strudel, *116,* 117
Stuffed Clams with Shallots and Lemon, 37

Stuffed Portobello Mushrooms, 114
Sweet-and-Spicy Roast Chicken, 64
Sweet Chipotle Drumsticks, 77
Sweet potatoes, Roasted Sweet Potatoes, Parsnips, and Onion, 154, *155*
Swiss cheese, Pan-Toasted Reubens, 31
Swordfish
　　Souvlaki-Style Fish Kebabs, 143
　　Swordfish Steaks with Caramelized Onions, 96, *97*

T

Tacos, Caribbean Shrimp Tacos, 35
Tarragon, Duck with Cherry-Tarragon Glaze, 87
Tartar sauce, Catfish Po' Boys, 144, *145*
Tarts, Frozen Coffee-Hazelnut Tarts, *192, 193*
Teriyaki sauce
　　Spicy Teriyaki Skirt Steak, 44
　　Tuna Teriyaki Burgers, 142
Tex-Mex Salmon Salad, 30
Thyme
　　Baked Whole Sea Bass with Fennel, 95
　　Oven-Fried Chicken with Buttermilk Brine, 73
　　Pan-Glazed Turkey Tenderloin, 84
　　Roast Tomatoes with Thyme and Olive Oil, *3, 41,* 169
　　Souvlaki-Style Fish Kebabs, 143
　　Striped Bass with Warm Sherry Vinaigrette, 101
Toasting spices, 25
Tofu, Tofu and Shiitake Stir-Fry, 115
Tomatoes
　　Beer-Braised Mussels, 147
　　Braised Beef Shanks with Wine and Shallots, *46, 47*
　　Braised Chicken Thighs with Tomatoes and Green Olives, 74, *75*
　　Butterflied Lamb with Couscous Salad, 58, *59*
　　Chicken-Chili Cobbler With Polenta, 80
　　Grilled Pork and Veggie Skewers, *134,* 135
　　Lobster Ravioli with Plum Tomato Sauce, 104
　　Mussels In Spicy Garlic Broth, 105
　　Niçoise-Style Tuna and Rice Salad, 27
　　Pasta with Chicken Sausage And Artichokes, 81
　　roasting, 169
　　Roast Tomatoes with Thyme and Olive Oil, *3, 41,* 169
　　Sautéed Escarole with Sun-Dried Tomatoes, 165
　　seeding, 104
　　Simmered Italian-Style Pork Chops, 51
　　Smoky Greens and Beans With Polenta, 120, *121*
　　Spaghetti "Bolognese," *10,* 112, *113*
　　Spinach and Sun-Dried Tomato Pizza, 149
　　Two-Tomato French Bread Pizzas, 128, *129*
Tortellini with Chicken and Watercress, *78, 79*
Tortillas
　　Quick Chicken and Black Bean Burritos, 138, *139*
　　Smoked-Chicken and Mango Wraps, 34
Truffles, Chocolate-Coconut Truffles, 190

Tuna
　　Niçoise-Style Tuna and Rice Salad, 27
　　Pan-Grilled Tuna and Lemons over Arugula, 94
　　Tuna Teriyaki Burgers, 142
Turkey
　　Coconut Turkey Fingers with Peach Sauce, 82, *83*
　　Grilled Turkey with Plums and Greens, *140,* 141
　　Pan-Glazed Turkey Tenderloin, 84
　　Pan-Toasted Reubens, 31
　　Spicy Blue Cheese Turkey Burgers, 85
Two-Tomato French Bread Pizzas, 128, *129*

V

Vanilla Bean Panna Cotta, 185
Vegetable-Cheese Frittata, 118
Vegetarian Avgolemono with Dill, 119
Vegetarian entrées. *See* meatless entrées

W

Walnuts, Broccolini with Walnuts and Shallots, *97,* 168
Wasabi paste, Poached Salmon with Wasabi Mayonnaise, *90,* 91
Watercress, Tortellini with Chicken and Watercress, *78, 79*
Whole grains, about, 6
Wine
　　Baked Whole Sea Bass with Fennel, 95
　　Braised Beef Shanks with Wine and Shallots, *46, 47*
　　Cinnamon-Poached Pears, 174
　　Duck with Cherry-Tarragon Glaze, 87
　　Filet Mignon with Garlic Cream Sauce, 40, *41*
　　Kielbasa with Cabbage and Caraway, 86
　　Pork Medallions with Marsala and Mushrooms, 54
Wraps, Smoked-Chicken and Mango Wraps, 34

Y

Yogurt, Frozen Coffee-Hazelnut Tarts, *192,* 193
Yukon Gold potatoes, Buttermilk-Scallion Mashed Potatoes, 156

Z

Zucchini, Grilled Pork and Veggie Skewers, *134,* 135

Dry and Liquid Measurement Equivalents

If you are converting the recipes in this book to metric measurements, use the following chart as a guide.

TEASPOONS	TABLESPOONS	CUPS	FLUID OUNCES
3 teaspoons	1 tablespoon		½ fluid ounce
6 teaspoons	2 tablespoons	⅛ cup	1 fluid ounce
8 teaspoons	2 tablespoons plus 2 teaspoons	⅙ cup	
12 teaspoons	4 tablespoons	¼ cup	2 fluid ounces
15 teaspoons	5 tablespoons	⅓ cup minus 1 teaspoon	
16 teaspoons	5 tablespoons plus 1 teaspoon	⅓ cup	
18 teaspoons	6 tablespoons	¼ cup plus 2 tablespoons	3 fluid ounces
24 teaspoons	8 tablespoons	½ cup	4 fluid ounces
30 teaspoons	10 tablespoons	½ cup plus 2 tablespoons	5 fluid ounces
32 teaspoons	10 tablespoons plus 2 teaspoons	⅔ cup	
36 teaspoons	12 tablespoons	¾ cup	6 fluid ounces
42 teaspoons	14 tablespoons	1 cup minus 2 tablespoons	7 fluid ounces
45 teaspoons	15 tablespoons	1 cup minus 1 tablespoon	
48 teaspoons	16 tablespoons	1 cup	8 fluid ounces

VOLUME	
¼ teaspoon	1 milliliter
½ teaspoon	2 milliliters
1 teaspoon	5 milliliters
1 tablespoon	15 milliliters
2 tablespoons	30 milliliters
3 tablespoons	45 milliliters
¼ cup	60 milliliters
⅓ cup	80 milliliters
½ cup	120 milliliters
⅔ cup	160 milliliters
¾ cup	175 milliliters
1 cup	240 milliliters
1 quart	950 milliliters

OVEN TEMPERATURE			
250°F	120°C	400°F	200°C
275°F	140°C	425°F	220°C
300°F	150°C	450°F	230°C
325°F	160°C	475°F	250°C
350°F	180°C	500°F	260°C
375°F	190°C	525°F	270°C

LENGTH	
1 inch	25 millimeters
1 inch	2.5 centimeters

WEIGHT	
1 ounce	30 grams
¼ pound	120 grams
½ pound	240 grams
1 pound	480 grams

Note: Measurement of less than ⅛ teaspoon is considered a dash or a pinch. Metric volume measurements are approximate.